Sawday's

Special Places to Stay

British Bed & Breakfast

"…a name well known to thousands of travellers who have sought comfort and hospitality in off-beat places"

The Guardian

Special Places

Pubs & Inns of England & Wales

"Sawday's handpicks the very best pubs and inns"

The Telegraph

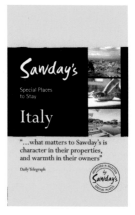

Sawday's

Special Places to Stay

Italy

"…what matters to Sawday's is character in their properties, and warmth in their owners"

Daily Telegraph

Sawday's

Special Places to Stay

Dog-friendly Breaks in Britain

Foreword by Kate Humble

Sawday's

Special Places to Stay

Twentieth edition
Copyright © 2018
Alastair Sawday Publishing Co. Ltd
Published in September 2018
ISBN-13: 978-1-906136-90-1

Alastair Sawday Publishing Co. Ltd,
Merchants House, Wapping Road,
Bristol BS1 4RW, UK
Tel: +44 (0)117 204 7810
Email: info@sawdays.co.uk
Web: www.sawdays.co.uk

Series Editor Alastair Sawday
Editor Carmen McCormack
Coordinators Sarah Barratt, Antonica Jones, Melissa Wiseman
Writing Claire Baranowski, Angela Barlow, Sarah Barratt, Tom Bell, Jo Boissevain, Nicola Crosse, Carmen McCormack, Sue Nottingham, Wendy Ogden, Honor Peters.
Thanks also to others who did a write-up or two.

Inspections Charlotte Barr, Sarah Barratt, Tom Bell, Nicola Crosse, Catherine Gledhill, Paul Hennessy, Carmen McCormack, Veronique Nelson, Caroline Nicholls, Diana Tamlyn, Gwen Vonthron, Melissa Wiseman
Thanks also to others who did an inspection or two.

Marketing & PR
Emily Enright, Tessa Glover
0117 204 7801
marketing@sawdays.co.uk

We have made every effort to ensure the accuracy of the information in this book at the time of going to press. However, we cannot accept any responsibility for any loss, injury or inconvenience resulting from the use of information contained therein.

Production: Pagebypage Co Ltd
Maps: Maidenhead Cartographic Services
Printing: Pureprint, Uckfield
UK distribution: The Travel Alliance, Bath
info@pelotongrey.com

Cover photo credits.
Front 1. Artist Residence London, entry 111 2. The Coach House at Middleton Lodge, entry 203
3. The Swan, entry 157
Back: 1. The Wheatsheaf, entry 83   2. The Queensberry Hotel & Olive Tree Restaurant, entry 1
3. The Globe Inn at Wells-next-the-Sea, entry 126
Spine: Augill Castle, entry 32

Sawday's

Special Places
to Stay

British
Hotels & Inns

4   Contents

5

According to the *Telegraph Travel* the top trends to look out for in the hotel and inn world this year are not so much about where you stay but what you will see, hear, do and smell – the experience of staying in a place. Pop up hotels, hotels with rooms in different countries, floating hotels, lifestyle hotels with a club house in which guests eat together at one table (buzzwords 'global community' and 'social architecture') are the latest fad.

Ironic that it hasn't taken very long for the big Online Travel Agencies to squeeze small, family-run hotels and inns – which are all about bringing people together – almost out of existence and now they will be reaping the rewards of a cool 're-invention'. And even more ironic that Sawday's already has a wonderful collection of small, mostly independent, places to stay and we've been 'bringing people together' for 25 years.

Another hot topic in hotels and inns today is food – traditionally a bit of an after-thought compared to getting the bedrooms right. Now we're a nation of foodies, hotels and inns have been forced to raise their game and make food as much of a draw as rooms. The small hotels and inns in this book have always taken food seriously. Some grow and rear their own veg and meat, bake bread and make marmalade. Many are committed to buying only local stuff 'except when it isn't good enough' one young inn keeper told me!

People who work in the hospitality industry have always been poorly paid. So we're delighted that yet another of these small hotels is committed to paying its staff the living wage rather than the paltry minimum, which is much fairer and better for staff retention. Happy staff make happy guests which creates a virtuous circle.

Pick any place in the book – some very smart, others more rustic. You won't get exactly the same experience anywhere but you will engage with friendly owners and staff, eat the best food, have an interesting experience and be looked after beautifully. You'll also come away knowing you've done your bit to help the local economy, wherever you've decided to lay your head. Who needs social architecture?

Alastair Sawday

Photo above: Tom Germain
Photo right: The Seaside Boarding House, Restaurant & Bar, entry 68

It's simple. There are no rules, no boxes to tick. We choose places that we like and are fiercely subjective in our choices. We also recognise that one person's idea of special is not necessarily someone else's so there is a huge variety of places, and prices, in this book.

Those who are familiar with our Special Places series know that we look for comfort, originality, authenticity, and reject the anonymous and the banal. The way guests are treated comes as high on our list as the setting, the architecture, the atmosphere and the food.

Inspections

We visit every place in the guide to get a feel for how both hotel and owner tick.

Photo: White House Hotel, entry 208

We don't take a clipboard and we don't have a list of what is acceptable and what is not. Instead, we chat for an hour or so with the owner or manager and look round. It's all very informal, but it gives us an excellent idea of who would enjoy staying there. If the visit happens to be the last of the day, we may stay the night. Once in the book, properties are re-inspected regularly, so that we can keep things fresh and accurate.

Feedback

In between inspections we rely on feedback from our army of readers, as well as from staff members who are encouraged to visit properties across the series. This feedback is invaluable to us and we always follow up on comments.

So do tell us whether your stay has been a joy or not, if the atmosphere was great or stuffy, the owners and staff cheery or bored. The accuracy of the book depends on what you, and our inspectors, tell us. A lot of the new entries in each edition are recommended by our readers, so keep telling us about new places you've discovered too.

However, please do not tell us if your starter was cold, or the bedside light broken. Tell the owner, immediately, and get them to do something about it. Most owners, or staff, are more than happy to correct problems and will bend over backwards to help. Far better than bottling it up and then writing to us a week later!

Subscriptions

Owners pay to be a part of Sawday's, but we only include places that we find special: it is not possible for anyone to buy their way onto these pages. Nor is it possible for the owner to write their own description. We will say if the bedrooms are small, or if a main road is near. We do our best to avoid misleading people.

Disclaimer

We make no claims to pure objectivity in choosing these places. They are here simply because we like them. Our opinions and tastes are ours alone and this book is a statement of them; we hope you will share them. We have done our utmost to get our facts right but apologise unreservedly for any mistakes that may have crept in.

You should know that we don't check such things as fire alarms, swimming pool security or any other regulation with which owners of properties receiving paying guests should comply. This is the responsibility of the owners. At some of our smaller places – particularly our inns – you should request a contact number for emergencies if staff are not present overnight.

Do remember that the information in this book is a snapshot in time and may have changed since we published it; do call ahead to avoid being disappointed. Our website www.sawdays.co.uk has all the latest information, plenty more photos and details of special offers too.

Photo: Knockinaam Lodge, entry 217

Finding the right place for you

All these places are special in one way or another. All have been visited and then written about honestly so that you can take what you want and leave the rest. Those of you who swear by Sawday's trust our write-ups precisely because we don't have a blanket standard; we include places simply because we like them. But we all have different priorities, so do read the descriptions carefully and pick out the places where you will be comfortable.

Maps

Each property is flagged with its entry number on the maps at the front. These maps are a great starting point for planning your trip, but please don't use them as anything other than a general guide – use a decent road map for real navigation. Most places will send you detailed instructions once you have booked your stay.

Symbols

These are explained at the very back of the book. They are based on the information given to us by the owners. However, things do change: bikes may be under repair or a new pool may have been put in. Please use the symbols as a guide rather than an absolute statement of fact and double-check anything that is important to you – owners occasionally bend their own rules, so it's worth asking if you may take your child or dog even if they don't have the symbol.

Wheelchair access ♿ – Some hotels are keen to accept wheelchair users into their hotels and have made provision for them. However, this does not mean that wheelchair users will always be met with a perfect landscape. You may encounter ramps, a shallow step, gravelled paths, alternative routes into some rooms, a bathroom (not a wet room), perhaps even a lift. In short, there may be the odd hindrance and we urge you to call and make sure you will get what you need.

Limited mobility – The limited mobility symbol 🚶 shows those places where at least one bedroom and bathroom is accessible without using stairs. The symbol is designed to satisfy those who walk slowly, with difficulty, or with the aid of a stick. A wheelchair may be able to navigate some areas, but in our opinion these places are not fully wheelchair friendly. If you use a chair for longer distances, but are not too bad over shorter distances, you'll probably be OK; again, please ring and ask. There may be a step or two, a bath or a shower with a tray in a cubicle, a good distance between the car park and your room, slippery flagstones or a tight turn.

Children – The 👶 symbol shows places which are happy to accept children of all ages. This does not mean that they will necessarily have cots, high chairs, etc. If an owner welcomes children but only those above a certain age, we have put these details at the end of their write-up. These houses do not have the child symbol, but even these folk may accept your younger child at quiet times. If you want to get out and about in the evenings, check when you book whether there are any babysitting services. Even very small places can sometimes organise this for you.

Pets – Our 🐕 symbol shows places which are happy to accept pets. Do let the owners know when booking that you'd like to bring your pet – particularly if it is not the usual dog! Be realistic about your pet – if it is nervous or excitable or doesn't like the company of other dogs, people, chickens, children, then say so.

Owners' pets – The 🐈 symbol is given when the owners have their own pet on the premises. It may not be a cat! But it is there to warn you that you may be greeted by a dog, serenaded by a parrot, or indeed sat upon by a cat.

Types of places

Hotels can vary from huge, humming and slick to those with only a few rooms that are run by owners at their own pace. In some you may not get room service or have your bags carried in and out. In smaller hotels there may be a fixed menu for dinner with very little choice, so if you have dishes that leave you cold, it's important to say so when you book your meal. If you decide to stay at an inn remember that they can be noisy, especially at weekends. If these things are important to you, then do check when you book.

Rooms

Bedrooms – These are described as double, twin, single, family or suite. A double may contain a bed which is anything from 135cm wide to 180cm wide. A twin will contain two single beds (usually 90cm wide). A suite will have a separate sitting area, but it may not be in a different room. Family rooms can vary in size, as can the number of beds they hold, so do ask. And do not assume that every bedroom has a TV.

Bathrooms – All bedrooms have their own bathrooms unless we say that they don't. If you have your own bathroom but you have to leave the room to get to it we describe it as 'separate'. There are very few places in the book that have shared bathrooms and they are usually reserved for members of the same party. Again, we state this clearly.

Meals

Breakfast is included in the room price unless otherwise stated. If only a continental breakfast is offered, we let you know.

Some places serve lunch, most do Sunday lunch (often very well-priced), the vast majority offer dinner. In some places you can content yourself with bar meals, in others you can feast on five courses. Most offer three courses for £25-£35, either table d'hôte or à la carte. Some have tasting menus, very occasionally you eat communally. Some large hotels (and some posh private houses) will bring dinner to your room if you prefer, or let you eat in the garden by candlelight. Always ask for what you want and sometimes, magically, it happens.

Photo: The Manor Town House, entry 268

Prices and minimum stays

Do check www.sawdays.co.uk or directly with the hotel/inn for the most up-to-date prices.

We quote the lowest price per night for two people in low season to the highest price in high season. Only a few places have designated single rooms; if no single rooms are listed, the price we quote refers to single occupancy of a double room. In many places prices rise even higher when local events bring people flooding to the area, a point worth remembering when heading to Cheltenham for the racing or Glyndebourne for the opera.

The half-board price quoted is per person per night and includes dinner, usually three courses. Mostly you're offered a table d'hôte menu. Occasionally you eat à la carte and may find some dishes carry a small supplement. There are often great deals to be had, mostly mid-week in low season.

Most hotels do not accept one-night bookings at weekends. Small country hotels are rarely full during the week and the weekend trade keeps them going. If you ring in March for a Saturday night in July, you won't get it. If you ring at the last moment you may. Some places insist on three-night stays on bank holidays.

Booking and cancellation

Most places ask for a deposit at the time of booking, either by cheque or card. If you cancel – depending on how much notice you give – you can lose all or part of this deposit unless your room is re-let.

It is reasonable for hotels to take a deposit to secure a booking; they have learnt that if they don't, the commitment of the guest wanes and they may fail to turn up.

Some cancellation policies are more stringent than others. It is also worth noting that some owners will take the money directly from your credit/debit card without contacting you to discuss it. So ask them to explain their cancellation policy clearly before booking so you understand exactly where you stand; it may well avoid a nasty surprise. And consider taking out travel insurance (with a cancellation clause) if you're concerned.

Arrivals and departures

Housekeeping is usually done by 2pm, and your room will usually be available by mid-afternoon. Normally you will have to wave goodbye to it between 10am and 11am. Sometimes one can pay to linger. Some inns are closed between 3pm and 6pm, so do try and agree an arrival time in advance or you may find nobody there.

Closed

When given in months this means for the whole of the month stated. So, 'Closed: November – March' means closed from 1 November to 31 March.

Photo: 94DR, entry 222

Sawday's

'More than a bed
for the night…'

Britain
France
Ireland
Italy
Portugal
Spain

www.sawdays.co.uk

Self-Catering | B&B | Hotel | Pub | Treehouses, Cabins, Yurts & More

© Maidenhead Cartographic, 2018

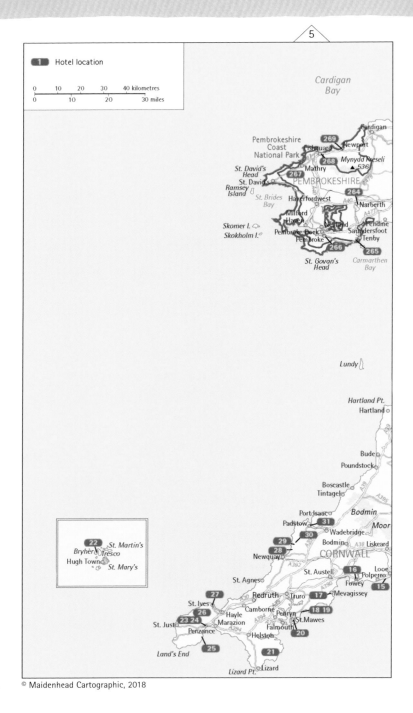

© Maidenhead Cartographic, 2018

Map 2   19

Map 4   21

© Maidenhead Cartographic, 2018

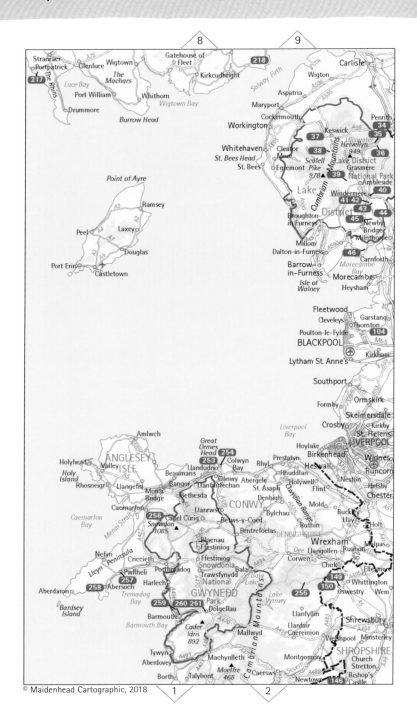

© Maidenhead Cartographic, 2018

Map 6

23

© Maidenhead Cartographic, 2018

Map 8

25

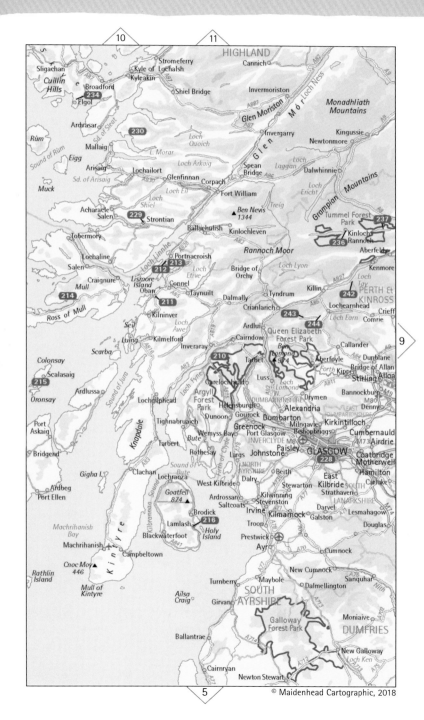

10 11

HIGHLAND

Sligachan
Cuillin
Hills
Broadford
234
Elgol
Stromeferry
Kyle of Lochalsh
Kyleakin
Shiel Bridge
Cannich
Invermoriston

Ardvasar
Sd. of Sleat
230
Glen Moriston
Invergarry
Monadhliath
Mountains
Kingussie
Newtonmore

Rùm
Sound of Rùm
Mallaig
L. Morar
Loch
Quoich
Spean
Bridge
Loch
Laggan
Dalwhinnie

Eigg
Arisaig
Sd. of Arisaig
Lochailort
Glenfinnan
Loch Arkaig
Corpach
Fort William
Loch
Ericht
Grampian Mountains

Muck
Loch
Shiel
Loch Eil
▲ Ben Nevis
1344
Treig
Tummel Forest
Park
237

Acharacle
Salen
229
Strontian
Ballachulish
Kinlochleven
236
Kinloch
Rannoch
Aberfeldy

Tobermory
Lochaline
Portnacroish
213
Rannoch Moor
Loch Lyon
Kenmore
Loch
Tay

Salen
Craignure
214
Lismore
Island
Oban
212
Loch
Etive
Connel
Bridge of
Orchy
Killin
242
PERTH &
KINROSS

Mull
Ross of Mull
211
Kilninver
Taynuilt
Dalmally
Tyndrum
Lochearnhead
Crieff

Seil
Loch
Awe
Crianlarich
243
Loch Earn
Comrie

Luing
Kilmelford
Ardlui
244
Callander

Scarba
Inveraray
Cairndow
Queen Elizabeth
Forest Park
Ben
Lomond
974
Aberfoyle
Dunblane

Colonsay
Scalasaig
215
210
Tarbet
Forth
Kippen
Bridge of Allan
Stirling
Alloa

Oronsay
Ardlussa
Garelochhead
Luss
Loch
Lomond
Bannockburn
Denny

Port
Askaig
Knapdale
Lochgilphead
Argyll
Forest
Park
Helensburgh
Dunoon
Gourock
DUMBARTONSHIRE
Drymen
EAST
Kirkintilloch

Bridgend
Tighnabruaich
Wemyss Bay
Greenock
Port Glasgow
Dumbarton
Milngavie
Bishopbriggs
Cumbernauld
Coatbridge

Gigha I.
Clachan
Tarbert
Bute
Rothesay
Largs
INVERCLYDE
Johnstone
Paisley
GLASGOW
228
Motherwell
Hamilton

Ardbeg
Port Ellen
Lochranza
NORTH
AYRSHIRE
West Kilbride
Dalry
Beith
Stewarton
East
Kilbride
Strathaven
Carluke

Machrihanish
Bay
Goatfell
874 ▲
Ardrossan
Saltcoats
Stevenson
Kilwinning
Darvel
LANARKSHIRE
Lesmahagow

Machrihanish
Lamlash
216
Brodick
Holy
Island
Irvine
Troon
Kilmarnock
Galston
Douglas

Cnoc Moy
446 ▲
Campbeltown
Blackwaterfoot
Prestwick
Ayr
Cumnock

Rathlin
Island
Mull of
Kintyre
Kintyre
Ailsa
Craig
Turnberry
Maybole
Dalmellington
New Cumnock
Sanquhar
Nith

Ballantrae
Girvan
SOUTH
AYRSHIRE
Galloway
Forest Park
Moniaive
DUMFRIES

Cairnryan
Newton Stewart
New Galloway
Loch Ken

© Maidenhead Cartographic, 2018

Map 10   27

Cape Wrath
Durness
232
A838
Bettyhill
Butt of Lewis   Port of Ness
Tongue
A851
Scourie
231
Altnaharra
Kinbrace
A894
Stornoway
Lochinver   Inchnadamph
Loch Shin
Portnaguran
L Erisort
Lairg
Cromalt Hills
Invercassley
Golspie
Sound of Shiant
Ullapool
Bonar Bridge
Dornoch
A837
Ardgay
A949
The Minch
Tain
Poolewe
Ben Wyvis
1046
Invergordon
Cromarty
Loch Maree
Wester
A835
A832
Garve   Dingwall
Black Isle
Fortrose
Uig
Rona
Kinlochewe
Achnasheen   Strathpeffer
Torridon
Muir of Ord
Beauly
Portree
233
Raasay
Torridon
Shieldaig
Lochcarron
Inverness

8

Map 12   29

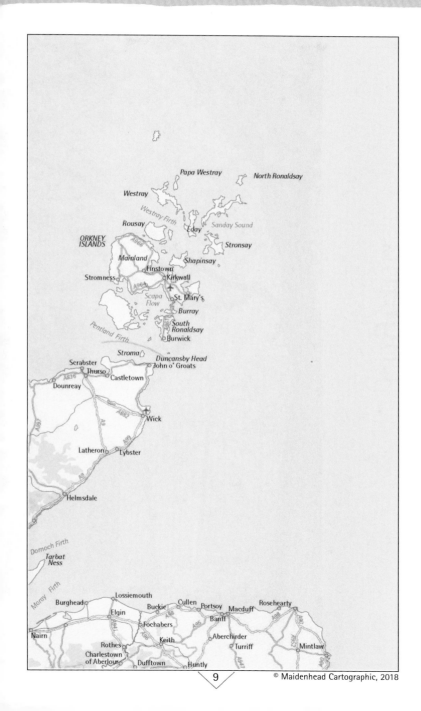

North Ronaldsay
Papa Westray
Westray
Westray Firth
Rousay
Eday
Sanday Sound
ORKNEY
ISLANDS
Mainland
Stronsay
Finstown
Shapinsay
Stromness
Kirkwall
Scapa
Flow
St. Mary's
Burray
South
Ronaldsay
Pentland Firth
Burwick
Stroma
Duncansby Head
Scrabster
John o' Groats
Thurso
Castletown
Dounreay
Wick
Latheron
Lybster
Helmsdale
Dornoch Firth
Tarbat
Ness
Moray Firth
Lossiemouth
Burghead
Cullen
Portsoy
Rosehearty
Buckie
Macduff
Elgin
Banff
Nairn
Fochabers
Rothes
Keith
Aberchirder
Mintlaw
Charlestown
Turriff
of Aberlour
Dufftown
Huntly

9

© Maidenhead Cartographic, 2018

England

The Queensberry Hotel & Olive Tree Restaurant

"No stilts, pogo sticks, space hoppers, flaming torches or whips in the bar." Such are the rules of the house, a nod in deference to the 9th Marquis of Queensberry, whose family built this street, and who wrote the rules of boxing in 1865. As for the hotel, it occupies four gleaming Georgian townhouses on a grand old street around the corner from Royal Crescent. It's an extremely comfortable base, with an elegant sitting room, a snazzy bar, a beautiful courtyard garden and some of the best food in town. Potter about and find fresh flowers, contemporary art, the daily papers, kind staff on hand to help. Bedrooms come in different sizes, but all are full of their own delights: Vi Spring mattresses, stylish fabrics, bold colours, flat-screen TVs. Smaller rooms overlooking the garden are lovely – size doesn't matter here – though one of the suites does come with a chaise longue in its super-stylish bathroom. Chris Cleghorn's delicious food waits below, perhaps langoustine tail with cheddar gnocchi and basil or anjou pigeon with celeriac, shallots and hazelnuts. Finish with a delicious chocolate and mandarin mousse served with stem ginger granita.

Rooms	16 doubles, 10 twin/doubles: £100–£300. 3 suites for 2: £260–£460. Extra bed/sofabed £25 p.p. per night. Valet parking, £14 per night – 50% off if booked direct.
Meals	Bar meals from £6.95. Lunch, set menu (Fri–Sun), £26–£32.50. Dinner, 3 courses, £49.50. Tasting menu available, 5-7 courses, £58–£80.
Closed	Never.

Laurence & Helen Beere
The Queensberry Hotel
& Olive Tree Restaurant
Russel Street, Bath, BA1 2QF

Tel   +44 (0)1225 447928
Email   reservations@thequeensberry.co.uk
Web   www.thequeensberry.co.uk

The Roseate Villa, Bath

The Villa is one of those lovely boutique hotels that scores top marks across the board. You're pretty much in the middle of town, but hidden away on a quiet side street opposite a pretty park. Then, there's a batch of smart bedrooms, which have style and comfort in equal measure. Add to this lovely staff on hand to book restaurants, balloon flights or day trips to Stonehenge and you have a perfect base. You're a five-minute stroll from magnificent Pulteney Bridge; the station isn't much further, so leave your car at home. You can hire bikes in town, then follow a towpath along the canal out into the country. Back home, there's tea and cake on arrival, buck's fizz for breakfast, even bats and balls for children who want to go to the park. Breakfast – served in an airy dining room – is excellent: smoked salmon and free-range scrambled eggs, buttermilk pancakes, the full cooked works. Rooms vary in size, but all have excellent beds, pretty wallpaper and sparkling bathrooms. Good restaurants wait close by. Don't miss the Roman Baths or the Fashion Museum. There's off-street parking, too, a real boon. *Minimum stay: 2 nights at weekends.*

Rooms	9 doubles, 11 twin/doubles: £99–£325. 1 family room for 4: £175–£475. Singles from £89. Extra bed/sofabed £45 per person per night.
Meals	Restaurant within 500m.
Closed	Never.

Caroline Browning
The Roseate Villa, Bath
Henrietta Street, Bath, BA2 6LX

Tel	+44 (0)1225 466329
Email	reception.trvb@roseatehotels.com
Web	www.roseatehotels.com/ bath/theroseatevilla

No. 15 Great Pulteney

You're on the grandest street in Bath, once home to Jane Austen; the Holburne Museum of Art stands at one end, Robert Adam's famous Pulteney Bridge at the other. As for No.15, it's a super-chic boutique hotel that doubles as a contemporary art gallery. You'll find collections of curios all over the place – art books, hand-blown lights, chandeliers by the score – then a golden bar for drinks before dinner, and a small spa with treatment rooms, a sauna and a hot tub in the original stone vaults. Bedrooms are sumptuous regardless of size, each with an original piece of art on the walls. You get Hypnos mattresses, cashmere throws, and stunning bathrooms, perhaps a copper basin, a walk-in shower or a claw-foot bath. Vast suites flood with light courtesy of high windows, while a help-yourself larder waits on the landing for popcorn, soft drinks and ice cream. Back downstairs, Café 15 offers delicious food all day: prosecco 'on the house' at breakfast, perhaps a feisty fish pie at lunch, then chicken with lemon and thyme at dinner. There's a small garden and a car park for guests, too. Hard to beat.

Rooms	25 doubles: £140–£500. 15 suites for 2: £250–£1200.
Meals	Lunch from £6.50. Dinner, 3 courses, £30–£40. Sunday brunch from £25. Afternoon tea £28.
Closed	Never.

Ian & Christa Taylor
No. 15 Great Pulteney
15 Great Pulteney Street,
Bath, BA2 4BS

Tel	+44 (0)1225 805879
Email	enquiries@no15greatpulteney.co.uk
Web	www.no15greatpulteney.co.uk

Abbey Hotel

A super central hotel with views to the medieval Abbey and gentle Somerset hills. Originally three Georgian townhouses, now its 62 rooms are bright, art-filled spaces – although not huge – best to choose one at the back if you want a quieter space. The feel is relaxed: chatty, professional staff look after you smoothly. Breakfast on croissants, bread from Bath's best baker, or cooked treats in the restaurant. Drink cocktails or a G&T – the gin list is impressive – in the cool ArtBar after a full day getting acquainted with lovely Georgian architecture or walking in the surrounding Cotswolds. Bath Abbey – fan-vaulted, imposing tower, stained-glass windows – is just across the square, the Roman Baths not much further; escape the crowds and walk over Pulteney Bridge for a gentle ramble beside the river Avon.

Rooms	46 doubles, 10 twin/doubles: £130-£500. 6 family rooms for 4: £200-£600.
Meals	Breakfast £10.50. Lunch from £7.50. Dinner, 3 courses, £35-£45; pre-theatre menu £21.50-£27.50 (5.30pm-7pm). Sunday lunch £24-£28.
Closed	Never.

Reservations Team
Abbey Hotel
North Parade,
Bath, BA1 1LF
Tel   +44 (0)1225 461603
Email   reception@abbeyhotelbath.co.uk
Web   www.abbeyhotelbath.co.uk

Bath Paradise House Hotel

The view here is sublime, a wide sweep across the city that's best observed on a sunny afternoon while tucking into afternoon tea in the garden. Not that you will spend your time looking out of the windows, even if most of the rooms do have the view: what you find inside is just as special. This is a hugely welcoming house with owners and staff who go out of their way to help you make the most of Bath. Downstairs, a smart sitting room has three arched windows framing the city and an airy breakfast room with Lloyd Loom furniture. Bedrooms are lovely, even the smallest, coveted by returning guests for its doors onto the terrace. Others are more substantial, especially those with bay windows that look the right way. You'll find four-posters, beautiful fabrics, warm colours, no clutter at all. Some have vast bedheads, others travertine bathrooms; bigger rooms have sitting areas, perhaps a claw-foot bath. Menu Gordon Jones, a very short stroll, is a top spot for dinner, while the occasional peal of bells comes from a nearby church. The Thermae Spa with its rooftop pool is a must. *Minimum stay: 2 nights at weekends.*

Rooms	3 doubles, 3 twins, 4 four-posters: £120-£175. 1 family room for 3: £130-£185. Singles £75-£120.
Meals	Restaurants in Bath 0.5 miles.
Closed	24-25 December.

David & Annie Lanz
Bath Paradise House Hotel
86-88 Holloway,
Bath, BA2 4PX

Tel	+44 (0)1225 317723
Email	info@paradise-house.co.uk
Web	www.paradise-house.co.uk

Combe Grove Hotel

This fine old house sits above Bath in 76 acres of woodland and gardens with views that stretch south for miles. It was recently bought by the Elmhurst Foundation (who offer apprenticeships) and plans are afoot to expand into a centre for health and wellbeing, with retreats, talks and meditation. As for Combe Grove, it's not your average hotel, but a place to wind down; you can have a massage, swim in two pools (one in, one out), join fitness classes from yoga to spin, book a personal trainer or lounge in the sauna and steam rooms, which are shared with country club members. There's a stylish bar serving fresh juices and homemade cakes, then an outside dining terrace, where you can play boules while waiting for your dinner. Big bedrooms in the main house have padded headboards and beautiful fabrics; garden rooms – most with terraces or balconies – have cool colours and fine walk-in showers. Food is served in the muralled dining room, perhaps roasted courgettes and red quinoa, a 28-day, dry-aged ribeye, lavender meringues with Jersey cream. Bath waits for shoppping and all things Jane Austen. *Minimum stay: 2 nights at weekends in summer.*

Rooms	28 doubles, 9 twin/doubles: £100-£280.
	3 suites for 2: £250-£370.
	Singles from £90.
Meals	Lunch from £6. Dinner, 3 courses,
	about £35. Afternoon tea from £15.
Closed	Never.

Sharon Love
Combe Grove Hotel
Brassknocker Hill,
Monkton Combe, Bath, BA2 7HU

Tel	+44 (0)1225 834644
Email	hello@combegrove.com
Web	www.combegrove.com

Cliveden House

Cliveden has no match in Britain, a country house of epic proportions that dates to 1605. It has been home to earls, dukes and one Prince of Wales, but it's best known for the Profumo affair, which almost sank a government; its famous pool and beautiful new spa are at your disposal. It sits in 376 acres of National Trust land with sublime gardens, marble fountains, sculptures by the dozen. You'll think you've arrived at Versailles and not without reason – the Astors bought Madame de Pompadour's drawing room and had it installed here! The Great Hall, a panelled masterpiece with vast portraits on its walls, is a fine spot for cocktails before dinner. Elsewhere, Corinthian columns, muralled ceilings and a dining room for ambrosial food, perhaps Orkney scallops, Anjou squab pigeon, rice pudding soufflé with Balvenie ice cream; there's a bistro in the old stables, too. Bedrooms, some in the main house, others in the wings, have huge beds, period art, white marble bathrooms. Some have hot tubs on private terraces, stately suites are vast, the riverside cottage is divine. Windsor is close.

Rooms	18 doubles, 10 twin/doubles: £445-£800. 19 suites for 2: £865-£1585. 1 cottage for 6: £2055-£2650. Extra beds £60 p.p. (no charge during school holidays).
Meals	Lunch from £8. Dinner, 3 courses, £55-£75; 7-course tasting menu £97.50. Afternoon tea £37. Sunday lunch £60.
Closed	Never.

Kevin Brooke
Cliveden House
Taplow, SL6 0JF
Tel   +44 (0)1628 668561
Email   reservations@clivedenhouse.co.uk
Web   www.clivedenhouse.co.uk

The Ginger Pig

Everyone loves this pub minutes from the beach. The décor is fresh, contemporary and open-plan and the food is consistently brilliant. Whether it's poached skate wing terrine, a chargrilled rib-eye with hand-cut chips, or a blackboard special (slow-braised lamb with spiced cabbage and garlic mash perhaps) this is a serious destination for those who love British food. The friendly team has created a balanced mix of drinking bar frequented by locals and dining area decked with modern art. It's all down to experienced restaurateur Ben McKeller who created the first in the funky, family-friendly Gingerman group. Upstairs: two floors of elegant new rooms with state-of-the-art bathrooms. Ginger cocktails await, as do super-comfy beds and posh coffee machines. The paved, sheltered garden is a little oasis. Breakfast (not included) can be taken in the pub's dining room and includes treats such as roast tomato rarebit and ham hock hash topped by a fried egg. Wander down to the seafront for a dose of ozone, or pop to Brighton for the buzz. *Minimum stay: 2 nights at weekends. Nearest car park on Princes Crescent, Hove, BN3 4GS.*

Rooms	8 doubles: £100–£150.
Meals	Breakfast from £6; full English £11. Lunch from £12. Dinner, 3 courses, from £25. Sunday lunch £15.50.
Closed	Never.

Ben Mckeller
The Ginger Pig
3 Hove Street, Hove BN3 2TR

Tel	+44 (0)1273 736123
Email	info@gingermanrestaurants.com
Web	thegingerpigpub.com

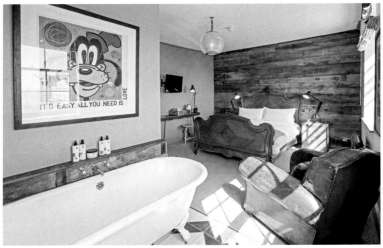

Artist Residence Brighton

At the top of a square, looking down to the sea, a cute hotel with an arty vibe. You're bang in the middle of Brighton with all the stuff you'd want on your doorstep: galleries, bars, the pier and the Royal Pavilion. As for the hotel, good food, great staff, relaxed informality and a playful style are the hallmarks here. You get stripped boards, exposed brick walls, and an old garage door that slides back to reveal a chic restaurant with an open kitchen. In typical AR style, it's now one of the best places to eat in Brighton – delicious tasting menus that get you talking as well as eating. You'll find cool art, the odd wall clad in corrugated iron, even an ornamental drainpipe! Bedrooms come in different styles. Some have Pop Art murals, others come in Regency colours, a new batch are super-cool with baths in the room. Most have small, stylish shower rooms, one has a decked terrace. There's a quirky bar for cocktails, a ping pong table that doubles as a boardroom, then lunch in the front restaurant with views through big windows down to the sea. The beach waits below. *Minimum stay: 2 nights at weekends.*

Rooms	17 doubles, 5 twins: £95–£250. 1 suite for 6: £280–£380. 1 quadruple: £145–£190. Singles £95–£165. Extra beds available.
Meals	Breakfast £2.50–£8. Lunch from £7. Dinner, 4 courses, about £30. Restaurants within 500m.
Closed	Never.

Charlie & Justin Salisbury
Artist Residence Brighton
34 Regency Square, Brighton, BN1 2FJ

Tel	+44 (0)1273 324302
Email	brighton@artistresidence.co.uk
Web	www.artistresidence.co.uk/ our-hotels/brighton/

Brightonwave

A small, friendly, boutique B&B hotel in the epicentre of trendy Brighton. The beach and the pier are a two-minute walk, the bars and restaurants of St James Street are around the corner. An open-plan sitting room/dining room comes in cool colours with big suede sofas, fairy lights in the fireplace and ever-changing art on the walls. Bedrooms at the front are big and fancy, with huge padded headboards that fill the wall and deluge showers in sandstone bathrooms. Those at the back may be smaller, but so is their price and they come with spotless compact showers; if you're out more than in, why worry? All rooms have fat duvets, white linen, flat-screen TVs and DVD/CD players; the lower-ground king-size has its own whirlpool bath and garden. Richard and Simon are easy-going and happy for guests to chill drinks in the kitchen (there are corkscrews in all the rooms). Breakfast, served late at weekends, includes pancakes, full English or sautéed tarragon mushrooms on toast. Good food waits on your doorstep: Riddle and Finns, The Salt Rooms, an Italian restaurant up the road. Fabulous Brighton waits. *Over 14s welcome.*

Rooms	3 doubles, 4 twin/doubles, 1 four-poster: £90–£190. Singles £75–£80.
Meals	Restaurants nearby.
Closed	1 week over Christmas & 2 weeks in January.

Richard Adams & Simon Throp
Brightonwave
10 Madeira Place,
Brighton, BN2 1TN

Tel	+44 (0)1273 676794
Email	info@brightonwave.co.uk
Web	www.brightonwave.co.uk

Drakes

Drakes has the lot: cool rooms, sea views and one of the best restaurants in town. It stands across the road from the beach, with the famous pier a three-minute walk. Inside, a cocktail bar doubles as reception, while a chic style has conquered all corners. Bedrooms are exemplary. Eleven have free-standing baths in the room, all have waffle bathrobes and White Company lotions, but what impresses most is the detail and workmanship. Handmade beds rest on carpets that are changed every year, contemporary plaster mouldings curl around ceilings like mountain terraces, and Vi-Spring mattresses, wrapped in the crispest linen, are piled high with pillows. Don't worry if you can't afford the best rooms; others may be smaller and those at the back have city views, but all are fantastic and the attic rooms are as cute as could be (one has a balcony). As for the food, it's some of the best in town, perhaps seafood chowder with razor clams, marinated wild boar with a quince purée, pineapple soufflé with lime and tequila ice cream. The Lanes are close and packed with hip shops. Don't miss the Royal Pavilion. *Minimum stay: 2 nights at weekends.*

Rooms	16 doubles, 1 twin/double: £120–£290. 1 suite for 2: £300–£360. 2 singles: £120–£160. Dinner, B&B from £92.50 p.p. Extra bed/sofabed available £25 p.p.p.n.
Meals	Breakfast £7.50–£15. Lunch, 2–3 courses, £20–£25. Dinner, 2–3 courses, £34–£45. Chef's Taster £60.
Closed	Never.

	Richard Hayes
	Drakes
	43–44 Marine Parade,
	Brighton, BN2 1PE
Tel	+44 (0)1273 696934
Email	info@drakesofbrighton.com
Web	www.drakesofbrighton.com

Bristol Harbour Hotel

You're in the heart of old Bristol, opposite St Nicholas' market, with Broad Quay at the bottom of the hill. As for this chic new hotel, it was once the home of two grand banks. The exterior stone work was modelled on the façade of St Mark's Library in Venice, but the interiors are just as good: a cool restaurant with high windows in one of the tiller's halls; a spectacular event space with 50 Corinthian columns in the other. There's a spa in the vaults which you enter through the door of an old safe, then a funky bar – once the bank manager's office – with gilded domes, ornate ceilings and flock wallpaper. Bedrooms come fully loaded: smart colours, fat mattresses, leather armchairs, decanters of sherry and gin. Bathrooms are a delight: walk-in showers, robes and White Company oils, perhaps a bath in the room. As for the Jetty Restaurant, expect fish and seafood in abundance, maybe fruits de mer and South Coast lobster; alternatively, try a twice-baked cheese soufflé, a rib-eye steak, a warm chocolate fondant with cherry ice cream. Bristol – often voted the coolest city in Britain – waits around you. *Minimum stay: 2 nights at weekends.*

Rooms	29 doubles, 10 twin/doubles: £155–£265. 3 suites for 2: £265–£655. Extra beds £20 p.p.
Meals	Lunch from £12.75. Dinner, 3 courses, £30–£40. Afternoon tea £15.95. Sunday lunch £19.95.
Closed	Never.

Grant Callaghan
Bristol Harbour Hotel
55 Corn Street,
Bristol, BS1 1HT

Tel	+44 (0)117 203 4445
Email	bristol@harbourhotels.co.uk
Web	www.bristol-harbour-hotel.co.uk

The Old Bridge Hotel

The Old Bridge is one of those places that mixes old-fashioned hospitality with contemporary flair, a template of excellence for others to follow. It's a big hit with the locals, who come for delicious food and exceptional wines, and it inspired the founders of Hotel du Vin, who were amazed how busy it was. Ladies lunch, businessmen converse, kind staff weave through the throng. You can eat wherever you want: in the beautifully refurbished restaurant; on a sofa in the lounge; or sitting in a winged armchair in front of the fire in the bar. You feast on anything from homemade soup to rack of lamb (starters are available all day), while breakfast is served in a panelled morning room with Buddha in the fireplace. It's all the work of owners John and Julia Hoskins. Julia's interiors are dreamy, with style and comfort going hand in hand. Beautiful bedrooms have fresh colours, chic fabrics, crisp linen, padded bedheads. All have posh TVs and robes in excellent bathrooms, some of which overlook the river Ouse. John, a Master of Wine, has a wine shop in reception; you can taste before you buy (and you will).

Rooms	18 doubles, 1 twin, 3 four-posters: £145-£230. 2 singles: £95-£125. Dinner, B&B £104-£150 p.p.
Meals	Lunch & dinner £5-£35.
Closed	Never.

John & Julia Hoskins
The Old Bridge Hotel
1 High Street,
Huntingdon, PE29 3TQ

Tel	+44 (0)1480 424300
Email	reception@huntsbridge.co.uk
Web	www.huntsbridge.com

The Crown Inn

A thatched inn built of mellow stone that stands on the green in this pretty village. Paths lead out into open country and you can follow the river up to Fotheringhay, where Mary Queen of Scots lost her head. Back at the pub, warm interiors mix style and tradition to great effect. The bar has stone walls, ancient beams, flagstone floors and a roaring fire; in summer you can decant onto the terrace and sip a pint of Black Sheep while watching village life pass by. Back inside, a beautiful new restaurant has recently appeared with golden stone walls, pale olive panelling and some very good food, anything from glazed ham and local eggs to oxtail lasagne, saddle of venison, sticky toffee tart with toffee sauce. You can also eat in the sitting-room bar on smart armchairs in front of another fire. Stylish bedrooms – some in the main house, others off the courtyard – are all different. You'll find smart colours, chic wallpapers, excellent bathrooms and good art. The bar hosts quiz nights, live music and the odd game of rugby on the telly, while on May Day there's a hog roast for the village fête.

Rooms	6 doubles, 2 twin/doubles: £73–£210. Singles from £55. Sofabed available, £30 per child per night.
Meals	Lunch & dinner £5–£25. Not Sun eve. Restaurant closed first week January.
Closed	Never.

Marcus Lamb
The Crown Inn
8 Duck Street, Elton,
Peterborough, PE8 6RQ

Tel	+44 (0)1832 280232
Email	inncrown@googlemail.com
Web	www.thecrowninn.org

Talland Bay Hotel

The position here is magical. First you plunge down rollercoaster lanes leaving the world behind, then you arrive at this lovely hotel and find a rather good view – a vast carpet of sea that shoots off to the horizon. Pine trees stand guard on one side, an old church crowns a hill on the other, then two acres of lawns roll down to a ha-ha before the land tumbles down to the bay. In summer, loungers and croquet hoops appear on the lawn, and you can nip down to a beach café for lunch by the water. Back at the hotel there's a conservatory brasserie, a sitting room bar and a roaring fire in the half-panelled dining room. You'll find art on the walls, polished flagstones, a terrace for afternoon tea. Follow the coastal path over the hill, then return for a good dinner, perhaps roasted scallops with caramelised orange, loin of venison with chestnut purée, lemongrass panna cotta with peach sorbet. Bedrooms have warm colours, vast beds, beautiful linen, the odd panelled wall. One has a balcony, a couple open onto terraces, all have lovely bathrooms. Gardens, beaches and the coastal path wait. *Pets by arrangement.*

Rooms	15 twin/doubles: £160–£290. 4 suites for 2: £260–£350. 3 cottages for 2: £210–£300. Singles £150–£340. Dinner, B&B £235–£425 per person. Extra bed/sofabed £45–£80 per person per night.
Meals	Lunch from £5.50. Dinner: brasserie from £12.95; restaurant £36–£42. Sunday lunch £21.50–£25. Afternoon tea from £6.
Closed	Never.

Stephen Waite
Talland Bay Hotel
Porthallow,
Looe, PL13 2JB

Tel	+44 (0)1503 272667
Email	info@tallandbayhotel.com
Web	www.tallandbayhotel.co.uk

The Old Quay House Hotel

You drop down the hill, weave through mazy lanes, then pull up at this boutique hotel which started life as a seaman's mission. It's a lovely spot, the estuary lapping behind the house and a waterside terrace for dinner in summer. Inside, uncluttered bedrooms flood with light; expect good beds, goose down duvets and elegant fabrics. Most overlook the estuary, eight have balconies (some tiny), the view from the penthouse suite is hard to beat. Bathrooms are just as good: white bathrobes, free-standing baths, perhaps a walk-in shower. Downstairs, super food waits in the restaurant, so take to the terrace for a cocktail, then dig into some delicious local fare, perhaps river mussels with wild garlic and shallots, stone bass with fennel and artichoke, poached rhubarb with white chocolate mousse. Fowey is enchanting, bustles with life and fills with sailors for the August Regatta. You can take the ferry across to Polruan where Daphne du Maurier lived, then walk over to Lantic Bay for a picnic lunch on the beach. Breakfast on the terrace, with local boats zipping past, is a treat. *Minimum stay: 2 nights at weekends in high season.*

Rooms	5 doubles, 5 twin/doubles: £145–£285. 1 suite for 2: £335. Singles from £105.
Meals	Lunch (Easter–October) about £15. Dinner £30–£37.50.
Closed	Rarely.

Julio de Carvalho
The Old Quay House Hotel
28 Fore Street,
Fowey, PL23 1AQ

Tel	+44 (0)1726 833302
Email	info@theoldquayhouse.com
Web	www.theoldquayhouse.com

Trevalsa Court Hotel

Trevalsa stands at the top of a cliff with sea views stretching far and wide. In summer life spills into the garden, where you can loll about in deck chairs and fall asleep in the sun. Explorations wait, too. You can nip down to a sandy beach or pick up the coastal path, which passes at the end of the garden; turn left for cliff walks or right for Mevagissey, an old fishing village of mazy lanes. Don't stray too far. Trevalsa is a treat: friendly, stylish, gently spoiling. Inside, the view is weatherproofed by an enormous mullioned window in the sitting room, a great place to watch a storm spin past. You'll find a small bar with colourful art, then a panelled dining room for tasty food, perhaps mussels steamed in Cornish cider, a bavette steak with a peppercorn sauce, treacle tart with brown bread ice cream. Bedrooms have warm colours, crisp linen, padded headboards, the odd wall of paper. Most have sea views, bigger rooms have sofas, all have excellent bathrooms, the suite has a private deck. Breakfast is served on the terrace in summer. The Lost Gardens of Heligan and St Mawes are close.

Rooms	7 doubles, 5 twin/doubles: £125-£275. 1 suite for 2: £205-£295. 2 singles: £70-£120. Dinner, B&B from £85 p.p. Extra bed/sofabed £20-£60 p.p. per night.
Meals	Dinner £31-£38.
Closed	20 November – 10 February.

Susan & John Gladwin
Trevalsa Court Hotel
School Hill, Mevagissey,
St Austell, PL26 6TH

Tel	+44 (0)1726 842468
Email	stay@trevalsa-hotel.co.uk
Web	www.trevalsa-hotel.co.uk

Driftwood Hotel

Gaze out to Gerrans Bay from the sheltered terrace where you eat breakfast in the sunshine. Wander the gardens, scramble down a wooded path to the beach and cove below. Hampers for beach picnics and rucksacks for walkers can be arranged; the seven-kilometre circular walk from Portscatho to Pendower Beach will take you across beach and through meadow. There's a fire to keep you cosy when it's chilly and a games room for children – special high teas too. Bedrooms vary in size and all except one have sea views, three have their own terrace. You'll eat well: Chris Eden heads up the Michelin-starred kitchen and service is on wheels. Take a digestif onto the terrace – on clear nights the sky is full of stars. *Minimum stay: 2 nights at weekends.*

Rooms	13 doubles, 1 twin: £185–£290. 1 cabin for 4: £235–£275. Dinner, B&B £125–£155 p.p.
Meals	Dinner, 3 courses, £65. Vegetarian tasting menu £75. Tasting menu, 8 courses, £85. Tasting menu, 10 courses, £105.
Closed	Early December to early February.

Paul & Fiona Robinson
Driftwood Hotel
Rosevine,
Portscatho, TR2 5EW

Tel	+44 (0)1872 580644
Email	info@driftwoodhotel.co.uk
Web	www.driftwoodhotel.co.uk

The Rosevine

Borrow backpacks and beach toys and stroll to the cove below, or find a spot to sit in the gardens facing the sea. This is a stylish hotel on the Roseland Peninsula where children are genuinely welcome and parents are spoiled. There's an adults-only lounge, a restaurant with tasty food, and an airy spaciousness all around. Choose between a studio or a family apartment. Studios are open-plan while apartments have separate bedrooms and bunk beds for children. Some spaces open to lovely terraces; the Slate Annexe studios are dog-friendly. Parents will appreciate the playroom with DVDs, games, toys and books, the table tennis and mini football pitch in the garden, and the children's tea party every day. Go rock pooling when the tide is out, paddle or swim when it's in and go sailing from Portscatho, a two-minute stroll away. Irresistible St Mawes is six miles away and ferries can whisk you to Falmouth for the day. *Minimum stay: 4 nights in high season.*

Rooms	7 studios for 2 with kitchenette: £152-£250. 8 apartments for 5 with kitchenette: £188-£390. Extra bed/sofabed £25 p.p. per night.
Meals	Lunch from £8. Dinner £29-£36. Afternoon tea £4-£15.
Closed	January.

Andries Loots
The Rosevine
Rosevine, Portscatho,
Truro, TR2 5EW

Tel	+44 (0)1872 580206
Email	info@rosevine.co.uk
Web	www.rosevine.co.uk

The St Mawes Hotel

Seaside chic, a relaxed feel and some lovely rooms are the hallmarks of this small hotel that stands on the water with big views out to sea. Outside, pavement tables are popular with people watchers, though those in the know head upstairs to the balcony, an unbeatable spot on a good day. Inside, you'll find sofas in front of the fire in the bar, and rugs on stripped boards in the colourful first-floor dining room. The food is delicious, the best local produce cooked simply, perhaps calamari with lemon mayonnaise, a crispy goat's cheese pizza, peanut butter brownie with vanilla ice cream. Beautiful bedrooms are scattered about, some with beautiful timber frames. Those at the front have watery views, all have chic fabrics, colourful art, the best beds, then robes and walk-in showers; a couple have baths, too. You'll find driftwood art scattered about, well-kept ales waiting at the bar and a small cinema for films if it rains. The harbour stands directly outside, so hire kayaks and explore the bay. Don't miss the castle or cricket on the beach. The coastal path starts at the front door. *Minimum stay: 2 nights at weekends.*

Rooms	7 twin/doubles: £140–£290.
	Cots/children in parents' room from £25.
Meals	Continental breakfast included,
	full English £8. Lunch from £6.50.
	Dinner, 3 courses, £25–£30.
Closed	Never.

Paul Goodwin
The St Mawes Hotel
Harbourside,
St Mawes, TR2 5DW

Tel	+44 (0)1326 270170
Email	stay@stmaweshotel.com
Web	www.stmaweshotel.com

Entry 20   Map 1

Bay Hotel

The Bay Hotel sits under a vast Cornish sky with views to the front of nothing but sea —
unless you count the beach at low tide, where buckets and spades are mandatory. Outside,
the lawn rolls down to the water. In summer it's sprinkled with deckchairs and loungers, so
grab a book or snooze in the sun and listen to the sounds of the seaside. Airy interiors are
just the ticket: stylish and homely with lots of comfort. The view follows you around,
keeping your eyes glued to the horizon. There are flowers everywhere, cavernous sofas, a
small bar for pre-dinner drinks. Bedrooms vary in size, one has its own balcony, all have sea
views (some from the side). Expect tongue-and-groove panelling, coastal colours, super
bathrooms and smart TVs. As for the food, lobsters come courtesy of the next door
neighbour, while the steak and kidney pie never leaves the menu. Try moules marinière, sea
bass with samphire, lemon and caper butter, Grand Marnier crème brûlée. Harbour cruises
often chance upon dolphins, seals, even basking sharks. You're on the coastal path, so bring
your boots, but don't miss afternoon tea. *Children over 4 welcome. Pets by arrangement.*

Rooms	6 doubles, 5 twin/doubles: £140–£280.
	3 suites for 2: £250–£330.
	Price includes dinner for 2.
	Singles from £105.
Meals	Lunch from £6.
	Dinner included; non-residents £34.95.
Closed	November – February.

Ric, Gina & Zoe House
Bay Hotel
North Corner, Coverack,
Helston, TR12 6TF

Tel	+44 (0)1326 280464
Email	enquiries@thebayhotel.co.uk
Web	www.thebayhotel.co.uk

Hell Bay

There are five inhabited islands here and many more that are completely empty, ranging from a jagged rock when the tide is in to beautiful sleek sand spits and your own little empire when it is out. Beach combers, adventurers, boat lovers and wild swimmers will find much to be happy about. The hotel food is stunning, most bedrooms face that sea view and the staff are the friendliest. You'll also find the family's modern art collection on the walls of the sitting room, including a Barbara Hepworth. Have a drink and an amuse bouche here before heading for the sea-facing dining room – try and time supper with the sunset. Splash in the pool, wander along the lanes to discover honesty shops selling honey, homemade fudge and fresh veg, an art gallery or two, cafés and a little post office that sells everything. Boats go to other islands most days – ten minutes to Tresco for the tropical gardens, a bit further to St Mary's which is livelier. *Under 2s free. Bags can be stored after check out until departure from Bryher.*

Rooms	25 suites for 2: £250-£640.
	Singles £175-£450.
	Dinner, B&B £140-£360 per person.
Meals	Lunch from £6.95.
	Dinner included; non-residents £45.
Closed	14 October – 16 March.

Philip Callan
Hell Bay
Bryher,
Isles of Scilly, TR23 0PR
Tel   +44 (0)1720 422947
Email   contactus@hellbay.co.uk
Web   www.hellbay.co.uk

Artist Residence Penzance

Artist Residence's Cornish offering is another cool bolthole from Justin and Charlie Salisbury. The vibe is laid-back: friendly staff stop to chat and you can turn up to dinner in your flip-flops. Choose where to eat – in the restaurant adorned with colourful pop art, in front of the wood-burner in the sitting room-bar or outside in the terrace garden. There's ping pong and table football to play while you wait for dinner from the smokehouse. Breakfast on French toast, local eggs and homemade granola before you whisk yourself off to St Michael's Mount, glimpsed from the hotel, or the Jubilee Pool lido. There's great surfing at Sennen and paddling at Porthcurno, both within ten miles, and you can catch the ferry to the Isles of Scilly direct from Penzance. *Minimum stay: 2 nights at weekends in summer.*

Rooms	14 doubles, 3 twin/doubles: £75–£180. 1 family room for 5: £185–£225. 2 triples: £135–£180. 1 suite for 2–3, with extra sofabed, kitchenette & sitting room: £190–£295. 1 cottage for 6: £270–£385. Singles £65–£120.
Meals	Lunch & dinner from £6; 3 courses £20–£25. Pub/restaurant across the road.
Closed	Never.

Charlie & Justin Salisbury
Artist Residence Penzance
20 Chapel Street, Penzance, TR18 4AW
Tel   +44 (0)1736 365664
Email   penzance@artistresidence.co.uk
Web   www.artistresidence.co.uk/
          our-hotels/cornwall/

Chapel House

Everything here is beautiful – a stunning Georgian house; views over town that stretch out to sea; bedrooms and bathrooms to rival those in the best designer hotels. All of which would be blossom in the wind without Susan, whose instinct to go the extra mile knows no restraint – this is not just a gorgeous house, but a friendly one, too. Outside, smart red bricks give some idea of the grandeur within, but step inside and find a contemporary wonderland that took two years to refurbish. The hall is home to works from the Newlyn School of Art, the double sitting room has high ceilings, an open fire and a baby grand piano, doors lead onto a balcony and down to a courtyard garden, a peaceful retreat in summer. Bedrooms are hard to fault: white walls soak up the light; handmade beds give a fine night's sleep; super-chic wet rooms have fabulous showers. One has a wood-burner in the room, another a bath under a glass roof that slides open. There's much more: delicious kitchen suppers at weekends; cooking demonstrations with local chefs; great restaurants along the road. The magical west coast waits.

Rooms	6 doubles: £150–£200. Singles £135–£150. Extra bed/sofabed £10–£25 per person per night.
Meals	Kitchen suppers on Friday/Saturday £22–£25 (or on request during the week). Sunday lunch from £14.50.
Closed	Rarely.

Susan Stuart
Chapel House
Chapel Street,
Penzance, TR18 4AQ

Tel   +44 (0)1736 362024
Email   hello@chapelhousepz.co.uk
Web   chapelhousepz.co.uk

The Old Coastguard

This seaside inn stands by the coastal path on the way into Mousehole, one of Cornwall's nicest villages, where kids play on the harbour's sandy beach at low tide. It's a peaceful spot with a clutch of restaurants and galleries, little disturbed since the Spanish raided in 1595. Roguish brothers Edmund and Charles Inkin have form when it comes to creating small hotels of character, and this place bears all their hallmarks, being good value and casual, with relaxed staff and great food. A diverse crowd of guests – couples, families, and ladies lunching – hang out in the rustic-smart bar and dining room. Conversation may stall as you take in the outlook over hydrangeas and palms to intriguing St Clement's Isle and beyond, across the sweep of Mount's Bay to the Lizard. With Newlyn a couple of miles down the road, locally landed fish features at breakfast. Supper, with a modern British slant, changes with the seasons. Retreat to a lime-washed bedroom hung with Cornish art – all vary in size, character and aspect, and eight have balconies.

Rooms	8 doubles, 3 twins: £140-£225.
	2 suites for 2: £245-£300.
	1 family room for 4: £200-£225.
	Singles £105-£132.
	Dinner, B&B £195-£300 for 2.
	Extra bed/sofabed £30 p.p. per night.
Meals	Lunch from £12. Dinner, 3 courses, about £30. Sunday lunch from £12.50.
Closed	1 week in early Jan.

Charles & Edmund Inkin
The Old Coastguard
The Parade, Mousehole,
Penzance, TR19 6PR

Tel	+44 (0)1736 731222
Email	bookings@oldcoastguardhotel.co.uk
Web	www.oldcoastguardhotel.co.uk

The Gurnard's Head

This quirky inn is one of the best – the sort of place a hiker hopes to find. Outside, the wild west coast weaves up to St Ives; secret beaches appear at low tide, cliffs tumble down to the water, wild flowers streak the land pink in summer. Inside, it's earthy, warm, stylish and friendly, with rustic interiors and fires at both ends of the bar. Logs are piled high in an alcove, maps and art hang on the walls, books fill every shelf; if you pick one up and don't finish it, take it upstairs to your very comfortable and pretty bedroom with a view over the Atlantic or the moors. A short, fresh and seasonal menu that changes daily will suit walkers who need a quick fuel stop as well as serious foodies and is served in the bar, dining rooms, or in the garden on sunny days. Choose from three hand-pulled Cornish ales, a choice of good ciders and more than 20 wines by the carafe.

Rooms	3 doubles, 4 twin/doubles: £125-£245. Singles £105-£132. Dinner, B&B £180-£245 for 2. Extra bed/sofabed £25 p.p. per night.
Meals	Lunch from £12. Dinner, 3 courses, £25-£35. Sunday lunch from £13.
Closed	Never.

Charles & Edmund Inkin
The Gurnard's Head
Zennor,
St Ives, TR26 3DE

Tel	+44 (0)1736 796928
Email	enquiries@gurnardshead.co.uk
Web	www.gurnardshead.co.uk

Entry 26   Map 1

Trevose Harbour House

This super-chic B&B started life in the 1850s as a fisherman's cottage. These days it's a small-scale version of a design hotel, pristine from top to toe. It's all the result of an 18-month renovation and it sits in the old town, a two-minute stroll from the beach. Inside, form and function rule the roost: everything is beautiful, nothing superfluous. Interiors come in blue and white with fresh flowers, local art, beautiful ceramics, and umbrellas in case it rains. Downstairs is open-plan – a small sitting room with an honesty bar concealed in a '50s dresser on one side, on the other a dining room where you sit at Ercol tables and tuck into an excellent breakfast under hanging lamps. Rooms have Hypnos beds, crisp linen, beautiful fabrics and impeccably upholstered armchairs. Three have sea views, all have smart TVs, coffee machines and hot-water bottles. Bathrooms are flawless: underfloor heating, walk-in showers, white robes and Neal's Yard oils, perhaps a claw-foot bath. Outside, labyrinthine lanes lead to the harbour, sandy beaches, art galleries and lots of delicious restaurants. Dreamy. *Minimum stay: 2 nights. Over 12s welcome.*

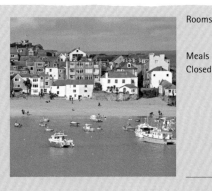

Rooms	5 doubles: £170-£290.
	1 suite for 2: £245-£290.
	Singles £170.
Meals	Restaurants 500m.
Closed	1 November – 12 April.

Angela & Olivier Noverraz
Trevose Harbour House
22 The Warren,
St Ives, TR26 2EA

Tel	+44 (0)1736 793267
Email	hi@trevosehouse.co.uk
Web	trevosehouse.co.uk

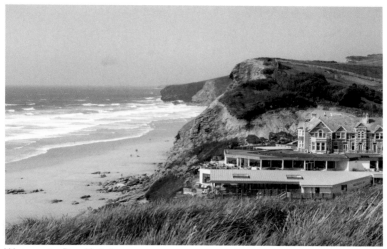

Watergate Bay Hotel

Grab a surfboard or a kite: this hotel kits you out to ride the waves. But you can still just lounge around, and if you have kids, it's a treat. Young children can make friends in the popular kids' zone while you disappear for a massage or a swim. It's all about the views here, with walls of glass in the huge café/bar, an infinity pool that gazes over the ocean, and a terrace strewn with loungers. This large hotel sits directly above one of the best sandy beaches in Britain — two miles long. There's a sitting room to head home to with an open fire, a hot tub with stunning views, and food that's fresh and delicious. Eat in the bar or Zacry's the grill, it's only 50 paces to the Beach Hut for a burger and Jamie Oliver's Fifteen Cornwall is right next door. Coastal light floods through the windows of the suites, the village apartments have their own kitchens and the ocean rooms are amazing.

Rooms	47 twin/doubles: £185–£345.
	2 suites for 2, 18 suites for 4,
	4 suites for 5: £285–£450.
	Singles £120–£268.
	Dinner, B&B £160–£335 per person.
Meals	Lunch £10. Dinner, 2 courses, £36.50.
Closed	Never.

Mark Williams
Watergate Bay Hotel
On the Beach, Watergate Bay, TR8 4AA

Tel	+44 (0)1637 860543
Email	reservations@watergatebay.co.uk
Web	www.watergatebay.co.uk

Entry 28   Map 1

The Scarlet

The Scarlet does what few others can – this may be a super-cool design hotel with one of the loveliest spas in the land, but the service here is fantastic: friendly, attentive, ready to help. As for the hotel, it sits above the sea with a vast wall of glass in reception to frame the view. Outside, you'll find a hot tub in the garden from which you can stargaze at night; inside, there's a stylish restaurant that opens onto a decked terrace, where you scoff delicious Cornish food while gazing out to sea. Elsewhere, an open fire in the sitting room, a pool table in the library, then a cool bar for Cornish wines and ales. Exceptional bedrooms all have sea views, then balconies or terraces, private gardens or viewing pods. Expect organic cotton, oak floors from sustainable forests, perhaps a free-standing bath or a huge walk-in shower. As for the spa, you get tented treatment rooms, chill-out pods that hang from the ceiling, and then a couple of swimming pools flanked by sunbeds. Finally, the hotel is green to its core, with a biomass boiler, solar panels and state-of-the-art insulation. *Minimum stay: 2 nights at weekends.*

Rooms	21 doubles, 8 twin/doubles: £210–£405. 8 suites for 2: £210–£460. Dinner, B&B £140–£280 p.p.
Meals	Lunch, 3 courses, £24.95. Dinner, 3 courses, £45.95.
Closed	Rarely.

	Meeche Hudd
	The Scarlet
	Tredragon Road,
	Mawgan Porth, TR8 4DQ
Tel	+44 (0)1637 861800
Email	stay@scarlethotel.co.uk
Web	www.scarlethotel.co.uk

Bedruthan Hotel & Spa

Bedruthan has the lot – stunning sea views, a couple of swimming pools, a spa with treatment rooms and restaurants galore. The sensory spa garden offers seven steps to heaven: a salt scrub; a sauna; a cold bucket shower; a dip in the hot tub; a wet scrub; a visit to the sky garden; a second bite at the hot tub. Adults get the run of the place in school time, then children come in the holidays and sign up to surf school. Qualified staff entertain younger children with fun crafty stuff or they can tire themselves out in the soft play area while their parents snooze on sunbeds by the pool. There's a wood-burner in the quiet sitting room, a cocktail bar that opens onto a terrace, then stylish bedrooms with retro colours and sparkling bathrooms. Some have separate rooms for children, others have terraces or sea views, a few overlook the car park. Younger children have early suppers, adults return later for a slap-up meal, perhaps guinea fowl, whole lemon sole, chilled strawberry soup with prosecco sorbet. The beach is a short stroll.

Rooms	36 twin/doubles: £160–£270. 27 suites for 6: £205–£490. 32 family rooms for 4: £175–£305. 6 singles: £75–£125.
Meals	Lunch from £6. Dinner £27.50–£32.50. Sunday lunch £14.50–£18.50.
Closed	2-31 January.

Janie White
Bedruthan Hotel & Spa
Mawgan Porth,
Newquay, TR8 4BU

Tel	+44 (0)1637 860860
Email	stay@bedruthan.com
Web	www.bedruthan.com

The Seafood Restaurant

In 1975 a young chef called Rick Stein opened a restaurant in Padstow. These days he has four more as well as a deli, a pâtisserie, a seafood cookery school and 40 beautiful bedrooms. Despite this success, his homespun philosophy has never wavered: buy the freshest seafood from fisherman on the quay, then cook it simply and eat it with friends. It is a viewpoint half the country seems to share – the Seafood Restaurant is now a place of pilgrimage – so come to discover the Cornish coast, walk on the cliffs, paddle in the estuary, then drop into this lively restaurant for a fabulous meal, perhaps black risotto with Cornish cuttlefish, grilled Padstow lobster with fine herbs, hot chocolate fondant with toasted marshmallow ice cream. Book in for the night and a table in the restaurant is yours, though flawless bedrooms are hard to leave. They are scattered about town, some above the restaurant, others at the bistro or just around the corner at St Petroc's House. All are immaculate. Expect the best fabrics, Vi-Spring mattresses, stunning bathrooms, the odd terrace with estuary views. *Minimum stay: 2 nights at weekends.*

Rooms	32 doubles, 8 twin/doubles: £165-£315.
Meals	Lunch £38.50. Dinner £58.50.
Closed	25-26 December.

Jill & Rick Stein
The Seafood Restaurant
Riverside, Padstow, PL28 8BY

Tel	+44 (0)1841 532700
Email	reservations@rickstein.com
Web	www.rickstein.com/stay/ the-seafood-restaurant/

Augill Castle

Augill is a one-off, a folly castle in beautiful country. It may look grand, but it's anything but – Simon and Wendy run their home with a rod of pure sponge. It's wonderfully informal and children love it. There are no uniforms, no rules, you just come to kick off your shoes and relax. You can do this in various places: on sofas in front of the fire in the hall; by a grand piano in the music room; in the honesty bar that opens onto a terrace; or in the cinema in the old potting shed. Breakfast is served communally in a vast dining room under a fine, ornate ceiling – local bacon, eggs from resident hens, homemade breads and jams. Elsewhere, panelled walls, roaring fires, books, art and antiques. Colourful bedrooms are all different. Some are enormous, one has a wardrobe in the turret, you'll find big bathrooms, bold colours and vintage luggage. Cottages are good for families and there's lots for children to do – dressing up boxes, five acres of gardens, a treehouse and playground, too. The Dales and the Lakes are close, but sybarites may just want to stay put. You can come to get married, too. *Minimum stay: 2 nights at weekends.*

Rooms	3 doubles, 4 four-posters: £160–£220.
	1 suite for 2, 1 suite for 4: £200–£320.
	3 cottages for 4: £220–£300.
	Singles from £100.
Meals	Dinner £25–£30. Supper platters £15.
	Afternoon tea £18.
	Children's high tea £10.
Closed	Never.

Simon & Wendy Bennett
Augill Castle
South Stainmore,
Kirkby Stephen, CA17 4DE

Tel	+44 (0)17683 41937
Email	enquiries@stayinacastle.com
Web	www.stayinacastle.com

Entry 32   Map 6

The Black Swan

A lovely small hotel in the middle of a pretty village that's surrounded by blistering country. It's all things to all men – a smart restaurant, a lively bar, pretty rooms – and very dog-friendly. A stream runs through the big garden, where you can eat in good weather; free-range hens live in one corner. Inside, chic country interiors fit the mood perfectly. You get fresh flowers, tartan carpets, games and books galore. There's a bar for local ales, a sitting-room bar with an open fire, but the hub of the hotel is the bar in the middle, where village life gathers. You can eat wherever you want – there's an airy restaurant, too – so dig into delicious country fare, with meat from the hills around you, perhaps a tasty home-made soup, Galloway beef and root vegetable stew, sticky toffee pudding with vanilla ice cream. Pretty bedrooms are fantastic for the money. Expect warm colours, beautiful linen, smart furniture, super bathrooms; one suite has a wood-burner. Stunning walking waits, the Lakes and Dales are close, children and dogs are welcome. A very happy place.

Rooms	5 doubles, 1 twin/double: £85-£115. 4 suites for 2: £120-£145. 6 annexes for 2: £105-£150. Singles £75-£140. 3 double bell tents available.
Meals	Lunch from £4.50. Dinner, 3 courses, £25-£30.
Closed	Never.

Louise Dinnes
The Black Swan
Ravenstonedale,
Kirkby Stephen, CA17 4NG
Tel   +44 (0)15396 23204
Email   enquiries@blackswanhotel.com
Web   www.blackswanhotel.com

Askham Hall

Askham is a dream, one of the loveliest houses in the Lakes. It's a Grade I-listed manor house with a 12th-century peel tower, but grand as it is, Charlie grew up here and it retrains the feel of home, making it a delightfully informal base. Expect contemporary art and open fires, a beautiful drawing room with an honesty bar, a small spa with an outdoor pool, then a café for lunch and gardens that open to the public. The hall sits in 40 acres of prime Cumbrian grazing land with paths that follow a river into glorious parkland. It's all part of the Lowther estate, where Charlie rears his own meat for Richard Swale's kitchen. As for the food, it's out of this world, ambrosial stuff that makes you want to move in permanently. You might find Askham pork cheek and barbecued hock, rough fell lamb with wild garlic risotto, Yorkshire rhubarb tart with brown butter ice cream; a kitchen garden and two polytunnels provide much for the table. Chic bedrooms have a cool country-house style (Prince Philip loved his). Some are vast, one has a tented bathroom, others have views to Knipe Scar. One of the best.

Rooms	11 twin/doubles: £150–£260.
	4 suites for 2: £250–£320.
	Extra bed/sofabed £35 p.p.p.n.
Meals	Lunch from £9. Dinner, 3 courses, £50;
	tasting menu, 5 courses, £65.
Closed	Sundays & Mondays. January – early
	February.

Charlie Lowther
Askham Hall
Askham, CA10 2PF
Tel   +44 (0)1931 712350
Email   enquiries@askhamhall.co.uk
Web   www.askhamhall.co.uk

Another Place – The Lake

This is a fantastic renovation of a fine old Lakeland hotel. It sits on Ullswater in 18 beautiful acres that roll down to the shore. Both house and water offer lots to do. You can paddle board on the lake, jump in for a swim, or set off to explore in a kayak. If that sounds too energetic, head back to the house for sofas to sink into and an indoor pool where walls of glass frame the view. The main building dates to 1714 and comes with ornate ceilings, marble fireplaces, the odd panelled wall. You'll find an airy restaurant for super food, a chic library with books and games, then sofas and banquettes in the 'living space,' where you can stop to eat, chill out by the fire, or slip onto the sun-trapping terrace, where views shoot across the lake to mountains soaring beyond. There's a gym, a hot tub, a sauna and treatment rooms, and forest school for kids. Rooms – some coolly traditional, others warmly contemporary – have fine beds, the best linen, robes in smart bathrooms. Most have the view, some have baths that look the right way. There's a kitchen garden, a croquet lawn, and wellies at the front door, too.

Rooms	28 twin/doubles: £160-£205. 6 suites for 2, 6 suites for 5: £235-£385. Singles from £120. Extra bed from £40.
Meals	Lunch from £7. Dinner, 3 courses, £40.
Closed	Never.

Alison Mathewson
Another Place – The Lake
Watermillock, Penrith, CA11 0LP

Tel	+44 (0)1768 486442
Email	life@another.place
Web	www.another.place/the-lake

Howtown Hotel

Welcome to Howtown, a world lost in time on a lane that goes nowhere on the quiet side of Ullswater. The position here is heavenly – water, mountain, field and sky – one of the best in the Lakes. The house sits in its own hamlet, dates to 1640, and has been welcoming guests for 117 years, a licensed farmhouse that has passed though five generations of the same family, who still run sheep and cattle on 400 acres of Lakeland fell. Inside, the past lives on: a panelled bar, William Morris wallpaper, smouldering coal fires, wall clocks and lots of brass. Homely bedrooms upstairs have simple pleasures: good beds, sheets and blankets, toile throws, fabulous views. Most are en suite, three have bathrooms one step across the landing. Dinner is old-school – you're summoned by a gong – then served at oak tables with a beautiful dresser at one end of the dining room. The food is a joy, perhaps Stilton soufflé, loin of venison, steamed marmalade pudding; there's a walkers' café and a locals' bar, too. David has an amphibious car for the odd lake cruise. Walks start from the front door. Matchless. *No email – phone enquiries only.*

Rooms	8 doubles; 3 twin/doubles each with separate bathroom: £208. 1 single sharing shower room: £104. 2 cottages for 5, 2 cottages for 7: £420-£800 per week. Price includes dinner for 2.
Meals	Lunch from £4.50. Packed lunches £8.50. Dinner included; non-residents £35. Sunday lunch £20.
Closed	10 November to mid-March.

Jacquie & David Baldry
Howtown Hotel
Ullswater,
Penrith, CA10 2ND

Tel	+44 (0)17684 86514
Web	www.howtown-hotel.co.uk

The Cottage in the Wood

This lovely restaurant with rooms is a great base for the northern Lakes. You're on the side of Whinlatter Pass with views that shoot off to a chain of Lakeland peaks – pre-dinner drinks on the terrace is hard to beat. Inside, chic interiors are just the ticket: the sitting room has a fire that burns on both sides, there are books and games to keep you amused, then windows galore in the restaurant. Rooms – some bigger, others smaller – have excellent beds, crisp linen and sparkling bathrooms. One in the eaves has a claw-foot bath, four have mountain views, the garden room has its own terrace. There's lots to do – lakes to visit, hills to climb, cycle trails to follow. Whatever you do, come back to Liam's fantastic food. His six-course tasting menu is a big draw; highlights include seaweed broth, langoustine with grapefruit, sweetbreads with wild garlic, fennel with olive oil jam. There's a drying room for walkers, secure storage for bikes and a burn that tumbles down the hill. Night skies amaze, red squirrels and woodpeckers visit the gardens. Two-night, midweek breaks are a steal and include dinner. *Minimum stay: 2 nights at weekends.*

Rooms	5 doubles, 3 twin/doubles: £110–£175. 1 suite for 2: £190–£205. Dinner, B&B from £100 p.p.
Meals	Lunch £35 (Thur-Sat). Dinner, 3 courses, £45; 6-course tasting menu £65. Not Sunday night.
Closed	January. Mondays.

Kath & Liam Berney
The Cottage in the Wood
Braithwaite,
Keswick, CA12 5TW

Tel	+44 (0)17687 78409
Email	relax@thecottageinthewood.co.uk
Web	www.thecottageinthewood.co.uk

Entry 37   Map 5

Borrowdale Gates

If you want deep peace, spectacular landscapes and a slice of luxury in a stylish hotel, you'll find it here. This is Borrowdale, an unchanged corner of the rural idyll, "the loveliest square mile in Lakeland" to quote Alfred Wainwright. High peaks encircle you, sheep graze the fields, the river Derwent potters past. The view from the top of High Seat is one of the best in the Lakes, with Derwentwater sparkling under a vast sky. Lowland walking is equally impressive: long or short, high or low, Borrowdale delivers. At the end of the day roll back to this lovely hotel. Big windows downstairs frame majestic views. You get binoculars, the daily papers, afternoon tea in front of roaring fires or out on the terrace in summer. Bedrooms are great value for money, with warm colours, super beds, smart bathrooms, a sofa if there's room. Some open onto terraces, several have small balconies, all have the view. As for the restaurant, a wall of glass looks out over the village and beyond, a fine spot for a good meal, perhaps hand-dived scallops, fell-bred lamb, lemon tart with cassis sorbet.

Rooms	18 twin/doubles: £214-£288. 3 suites for 2: £262-£318. 4 singles: £100-£116. Price includes dinner.
Meals	Light lunch from £8. Dinner included; non-residents £34.50-£43. Afternoon tea from £15. Sunday lunch £25.
Closed	3-19 January.

	Ross Harper Borrowdale Gates Grange-in-Borrowdale, Keswick, CA12 5UQ
Tel	+44 (0)17687 77204
Email	hotel@borrowdale-gates.com
Web	www.borrowdale-gates.com

Lancrigg

There's nothing stuffy about this rambling old house on a hillside bang in the middle of the Lake District. A friendly informality pervades the place, so everyone will feel completely at home, from families with young ones to lone walkers. You can drink and snack in the cosy and stylish Poet's Bar, once the old library, or get down to more serious eating in the dining room. This is where the hotel's chef creates imaginative feasts, inspired by vintage recipes, using the very best of local, seasonal ingredients. Simon and his friendly staff look after you well. While the kids run wild in the woodland playground, relax in the sitting room by the fire, drink in those outstanding views, and tell yourself you're going to go for a bracing walk soon. Wordsworth found this house an inspiring place to stay, and so will you. *Minimum stay: 2 nights at weekends.*

Rooms	5 doubles, 3 twins, 2 family rooms for 4: £79–£220. Extra bed/sofabed £30–£45 p.p.p.n.
Meals	Breakfast £8–£12. Lunch from £12.95. Dinner à la carte, 4 courses, £39.95.
Closed	15 January to early February.

Alison Drury
Lancrigg
Easedale Road,
Grasmere, LA22 9QN
Tel   +44 (0)15394 35317
Email   info@lancrigg.co.uk
Web   www.lancrigg.co.uk

Cedar Manor Hotel

A small country house on the edge of Windermere with good prices, pretty interiors and delicious food. Jonathan and Caroline love their world and can't stop spending money on it. They recently added a smart terrace at the front, turned the office into another sitting room, and put in a couple of fancy bathrooms. This 17th-century house was once home to a retired vicar, hence the ecclesiastic windows. Outside, an ancient cedar of Lebanon shades the lawn. Inside, cool colours and an easy style flow throughout. The big sitting room doubles as the bar and comes in browns and creams with sofas and local art. Bedrooms – some warmly traditional, others nicely contemporary – have Zoffany fabrics, Lloyd Loom wicker and flat-screen TVs; most have fancy bathrooms, some have big views, the bathroom in the coach-house suite is out of this world. You eat in a pretty dining room with views to the front or on the terrace in good weather, perhaps goat's cheese with a red pepper mousse, local lamb with tarragon gnocchi, warm chocolate fudge cake with real-ale ice cream. All things Windermere are on your doorstep. *Minimum stay: 2 nights at weekends.*

Rooms	7 doubles, 1 twin: £145–£245.
	2 suites for 2: £245–£475.
	Singles £125–£455.
	Dinner, B&B £170–£500 per person.
Meals	Dinner £32.95–£39.95.
Closed	Rarely.

Jonathan & Caroline Kaye
Cedar Manor Hotel
Ambleside Road,
Windermere, LA23 1AX

Tel	+44 (0)15394 43192
Email	info@cedarmanor.co.uk
Web	www.cedarmanor.co.uk

Linthwaite House

The hotel sits perched on a hill with views over Windermere, woods and peaks. Smartly-dressed staff greet you as you park your car and take you through newly-planted gardens to the front door of this Arts and Crafts house. Service is on wheels here. Chef Ritu Dalmia is in charge of the kitchen and her passion for Italian food is evident, only made better by such good local ingredients. Visit the Lakes Library to plan your days: boat trips, steam trains, walks near and far, visits to Cartmel, Hilltop or Grasmere. You don't really need to lift a finger, it can all be organised for you. There are mountain bikes to borrow, wellies to put on; fishing can be sorted either in the hotel's own tarn or further afield – one-to-one fly fishing lessons too. The gardens will be stunning when they have become more established, the terrace is a dreamy place to sit with a drink and in the autumn the spa will be completed. This is an indulgent sort of place that people like to return to year after year.

Rooms	30 twin/doubles: £306–£454.
	4 suites for 2: £492–£684.
Meals	Lunch, 3 courses, from £24.95.
	Dinner, 3 courses à la carte, £58.
Closed	Rarely.

Harry Fernandes
Linthwaite House
Crook Road, Bowness-on-Windermere,
Windermere, LA23 3JA

Tel   +44 (0)15394 88600
Email   stay@linthwaitehouse.com
Web   www.linthwaitehouse.com

Gilpin Hotel

Gilpin is one of the loveliest places to stay in the country, simple as that. It's a family affair and delivers at every turn, its staff delightful, its Michelin-starred food divine, its interiors a treasure trove of beautiful things. It is one of those rare places that never stands still and recent additions include five stunning spa chalets above a small lake and a second restaurant serving pan-Asian food. Despite all this, it remains an English country-house hotel. A cool elegance flows throughout with smouldering fires, Zoffany wallpapers, gilded mirrors, flowers everywhere. An elegant sitting room runs into a chic bar, where doors open onto a terrace for Pimm's in the sun; magnolia trees, cherry blossom and a copper beech wait in the 20-acre garden. Bedrooms are divine: crisp linen, smart fabrics, robes in beautiful bathrooms. The garden suites have hot tubs, the spa suites have saunas, too. As for the food, it's all whisked up by Hrishikesh Desai (who won Chefs On Trial to land his job), perhaps chilli-glazed lobster, spring lamb with masala sauce, Yorkshire rhubarb with Bergamot panna cotta. *Minimum stay: 2 nights at weekends.*

Rooms	8 doubles, 12 twin/doubles: £365–£715. 6 suites for 2, 5 suites for 2 (spa chalets on the lake): £545–£715. Price includes dinner for 2. Special rates for three or more nights.
Meals	Dinner included; non-residents £70. Sunday lunch, £35. Tasting menu, £90. Afternoon tea from £22.50.
Closed	Never.

John, Christine, Barnaby & Zoe Cunliffe
Gilpin Hotel
Crook Road,
Windermere, LA23 3NE

Tel	+44 (0)15394 88818
Email	hotel@thegilpin.co.uk
Web	www.thegilpin.co.uk

Gilpin Lake House & Spa

Every now and then you bump into a hotel that knocks your socks off, and Gilpin Lake House does just that. This is an extraordinary place – a tiny spa hotel with only six rooms, luxury and intimacy entwined. It sits away from the crowds, lost in the hills, surrounded by acres of peaceful woodland. A swimming pool in the house opens onto a terrace, where you can flop on loungers and gaze down on the lake. Elsewhere, beautiful gardens, a rowing boat, and a second hot tub overlooking fells. There's a treatment room in a cabin that sits above the lake, and a snug boathouse with a deck on the water. As for the house, you'll find sofas in front of a wood-burner in the sitting room, lake views, books galore and beautiful art. Spoiling rooms have fabulous beds, sofas, beautiful fabrics, bathrooms that don't hold back. Breakfast is served wherever you want: your room, the terrace, the conservatory. There's a chauffeur to whizz you up to their sister hotel for dinner (included in the price). Come with friends and take the whole place. Out of this world. *Minimum stay: 2 nights at weekends, 3 nights bank holidays & Easter. Children over 7 welcome.*

Rooms	6 twin/doubles: £495-£605. Price includes dinner for 2 at Gilpin Hotel, chauffeur included!
Meals	Dinner included; non-residents £70. Sunday lunch, £35. Tasting menu, £90. Afternoon tea from £22.50.
Closed	Never.

John, Christine, Barnaby & Zoe Cunliffe
Gilpin Lake House & Spa
Crook, Windermere, LA8 8LN

Tel	+44 (0)15394 88818
Email	hotel@thegilpin.co.uk
Web	www.thegilpin.co.uk/lake-house

The Punch Bowl Inn

This gorgeous inn is hard to beat. You're in the hills above Windermere in a pretty village encircled by lanes that defeat most tourists. It's deeply rural with ten-mile views down the valley and a church next door; there's a bench to drink in the view, bell ringers practise on Friday mornings, the occasional bride glides out in summer. As for the Punch Bowl, it was rescued from neglect, renovated beautifully, and now sparkles, a stylish mix of old and new. Outside, honeysuckle and roses ramble on stone walls. Inside, rustic elegance runs throughout: Farrow & Ball colours, rugs on wood floors, sofas in front of the wood-burner. Arthur Bridgeman Quin's ambrosial food is a big draw, perhaps Lancashire cheese soufflé, Cumbrian venison with smoked beetroot, banana soufflé with vanilla ice cream. Chic bedrooms hit the spot, with beautiful linen, pretty fabrics and Roberts radios. Excellent bathrooms have double-ended baths, separate showers and white robes. Four have the view, the suite is enormous, smaller rooms are nicely priced. There's a terrace for lunch in the sun, too.

Rooms	5 doubles, 2 twin/doubles, 1 four-poster: £105–£235. 1 suite for 2: £235–£305. Singles from £85.
Meals	Lunch from £5. Dinner, 3 courses, £30–£35.
Closed	Never.

Richard Rose
The Punch Bowl Inn
Crosthwaite, Kendal, LA8 8HR

Tel	+44 (0)15395 68237
Email	info@the-punchbowl.co.uk
Web	www.the-punchbowl.co.uk

Entry 44   Map 5

The Masons Arms

The Masons is a Lakeland institution, an ancient inn lost in blissful country. You're on the side of a hill with 15-mile views across a quilt of fields to Scout Scar; in summer, pub life decants onto a beautiful terrace – a sitting room in the sun – where window boxes and flowerbeds tumble with colour. The inn dates to the 16th century and is impossibly pretty. The bar is gorgeous, with low ceilings, wavy beams, flagged floors and roaring fires, then splendid local ales to quench your thirst. Rustic elegance upstairs comes courtesy of stripped floors, country rugs and red walls in the first-floor dining room, so grab a window seat for fabulous views and dig into local fare, perhaps cheese soufflé, haunch of venison, toffee and banana sundae. Rooms (in the main house) and cottages (off the courtyard, great for families) are a steal. All have comfort and style in spades. You'll find lovely beds, pretty fabrics and super bathrooms; several have private terraces, too. As befitting a community local, events are often on the menu: live music, a food market, even the odd busker. Cartmel Priory is close. *Minimum stay: 2 nights at weekends.*

Rooms	5 apartments for 2: £95–£140. 1 cottage for 4, 1 cottage for 6: £130–£185. Travel cots/extra beds from £10.
Meals	Breakfast & lunch from £4.95. Bar meals from £9.95. Dinner, 3 courses, £25–£30. Sunday lunch from £12.95.
Closed	Never.

John & Diane Taylor
The Masons Arms
Strawberry Bank, Cartmell Fell,
Grange-over-Sands, LA11 6NW

Tel	+44 (0)15395 68486
Email	info@masonsarmsstrawberrybank.co.uk
Web	www.masonsarmsstrawberrybank.co.uk

Aynsome Manor Hotel

A small country house with a big heart. It may not be the grandest place in the book but the welcome is genuine, the peace is intoxicating and the value unmistakable. From the front, a long sweep across open meadows leads south to Cartmel and its priory, a view that has changed little in 800 years. The house, a mere pup by comparison, dates to 1512. Step in to find red armchairs, a grandfather clock and a coal fire in the hall. There's a small bar for a dram at the front and a cantilever staircase with cupola dome that sweeps you up to a first-floor drawing room, where panelled windows frame the view. Downstairs, you eat under a wildly ornate ceiling with Georgian colours and old portraits on the walls. You get lovely country cooking, too: French onion soup, roast leg of Cumbrian lamb, rich chocolate mousse served with white chocolate sauce. Bedrooms are simple, spotless, cosy and colourful. Some have views over the fields, one may be haunted, all have good bathrooms. Staff are lovely, nothing is too much trouble, kippers with lemon at breakfast are a treat. Windermere and Coniston are close.

Rooms	5 doubles, 7 twins, 1 family room for 4: £90–£160. Singles £85–£145. Dinner, B&B £75–£97 per person. Extra bed/sofabed £45–£55 per person per night.
Meals	Packed lunches by arrangement £9.50. Dinner, 4 courses, £33.
Closed	Christmas, 2-30 January.

Christopher & Andrea Varley
Aynsome Manor Hotel
Aynsome Lane, Cartmel,
Grange-over-Sands, Cumbria, LA11 6HH

Tel	+44 (0)15395 36653
Email	aynsomemanor@btconnect.com
Web	www.aynsomemanorhotel.co.uk

The Sun Inn

This fine old inn sits between the Dales and the Lakes in an ancient market town, one of the prettiest in the north. It backs onto St Mary's churchyard, where wild flowers flourish, and on the far side you'll find "the fairest view in England" to quote John Ruskin. Herons fish the river, lambs graze the fells beyond, a vast sky hangs above. Turner came to paint it in 1825 and benches wait for those who want to linger. As for the Sun, it does what all good inns do, it looks after you in style. It dates to 1670 and started life as a butcher's. Inside, there's lots of pretty old stuff – stone walls, rosewood panelling, wood-burners working overtime – then warm colours, fresh flowers and the daily papers. You'll find leather banquettes, local art and dining-room chairs from Cunard's Mauretania, so eat in style, perhaps goat's cheese with honey, hogget with onion jam, banana parfait with chocolate sorbet. Rooms have good beds, smart fabrics, robes in spotless bathrooms. Parking permits come with your room and can be used far and wide. Market day is Thursday, dogs are welcome, don't miss Sunday lunch. *Minimum stay: 2 nights on weekends.*

Rooms	9 doubles, 2 twin/doubles: £135-£189. Dinner, B&B from £90 p.p. Singles from £85. Extra beds £20.
Meals	Lunch from £6; not Monday. Dinner, £21-£34. Sunday lunch from £14.50.
Closed	Never.

Iain & Jenny Black
The Sun Inn
6 Market Street, Kirkby Lonsdale,
Carnforth, LA6 2AU

Tel	+44 (0)15242 71965
Email	email@sun-inn.info
Web	www.sun-inn.info

Entry 47   Map 6

Cavendish Hotel

The Cavendish has impeccable credentials. It stands on the Chatsworth Estate, is owned by the Duke and Duchess of Devonshire, and Chatsworth House itself stands a mile or two across the fields from this smart hotel. All of which means you can rise leisurely, have a good breakfast, then follow paths across to one of Britain's loveliest houses where fine gardens and a jaw-dropping art collection wait. As for the hotel, it has a warm country-house feel: sofas in front of the fire in the sitting room; art from the 'big house' on the walls; afternoon tea served on the lawn in summer. Bedrooms mix pretty florals with period colours and smart fabrics. None are small, all but one have country views, some are rather swanky. You get robes in excellent bathrooms, a sofa if there's room, crisp linen on comfy beds. Downstairs you can eat in the Garden Room or out on its terrace (more informal, lovely views) or in the elegant restaurant, perhaps hand-dived scallops, haunch of venison, Granny Smith apple crumble. Outside, the Peak District waits for walkers, while fishing can be arranged.

Rooms	20 doubles, 2 twins: £250-£305.
	1 suite for 2: £375.
	1 family room for 4: £250-£305.
	Singles £179-£234.
Meals	Continental breakfast £9.70;
	full English £18.90. Lunch from £6.
	Dinner £30-£45.
Closed	Never.

Philip Joseph
Cavendish Hotel
Church Lane, Baslow,
Bakewell, DE45 1SP

Tel	+44 (0)1246 582311
Email	info@cavendish-hotel.net
Web	www.cavendish-hotel.net

The Peacock at Rowsley

The Peacock sits between two fine houses, Haddon Hall and Chatsworth House. You can follow rivers up to each – the Derwent to Chatsworth, the Wye to the hall – both a stroll through beautiful parkland. As for the hotel, it was built in 1652 and was home to the steward of Haddon. Inside, old and new mix gracefully: mullioned windows, hessian rugs, aristocratic art, then striking colours that give a contemporary feel. You'll find Mouseman tables and chairs in the restaurant, where French windows open onto the terrace. Elsewhere, a fire smoulders in the bar every day, the daily papers wait in the sitting room, the garden lawn runs down to the river. Stylish bedrooms have crisp linen, good beds, Farrow & Ball colours, the odd antique; one has a bed from Belvoir Castle. Good food waits in the restaurant, with meat and game from the estate, perhaps venison terrine, roast partridge, Bakewell Tart with buttermilk ice cream. There's afternoon tea in the garden in summer and you can fish both rivers, with day tickets available from reception. Guests also receive a discount on entry to Haddon Hall. *Minimum stay: 2 nights at weekends.*

Rooms	10 doubles, 2 four-posters: £205–£310. 1 suite for 2: £250–£310. 2 singles: £130–£145.
Meals	Lunch from £4.50. Dinner £60. Sunday lunch £22.50–£29.50.
Closed	Rarely.

Laura Ball
The Peacock at Rowsley
Bakewell Road, Rowsley,
Matlock, DE4 2EB

Tel	+44 (0)1629 733518
Email	reception@thepeacockatrowsley.com
Web	www.thepeacockatrowsley.com

Loyton Lodge

You get the impression the tiny lanes that wrap around this small estate act as a sort of fortification, one designed to confuse invaders and protect this patch of heaven. And heaven it is – 280 acres of rolling hills and ancient woodland, with wild flowers, pristine rivers, strutting pheasants and the odd red deer commuting across the fields. It's England circa 1964 with nothing but birdsong to break the peace and glorious walks that start at the front door. As for Loyton, it's a great little base for a night or two deep in the hills. It mixes contemporary interiors with an old-school feel – roaring fires, comfy sofas, wonderful art, even a snooker room. Bedrooms have warm colours and smart fabrics, perhaps a sleigh bed or a claw-foot bath, then books and robes and crisp white linen. Breakfast is a treat – bacon and sausages from home-reared pigs, eggs from estate hens – and there's dinner by arrangement, perhaps local asparagus, lemon sole, walnut and fruit crumble. Take the whole house and bring the family or come for the odd night of live jazz. Exmoor waits, as do good local restaurants.

Rooms	7 doubles, 2 twin/doubles, 1 twin: £95–£130. Singles from £80. Extra beds £20, under 12s free.
Meals	Dinner, 3 courses, about £30, by arrangement.
Closed	Rarely.

Isobel, Sally & Angus Barnes
Loyton Lodge
Morebath,
Tiverton, EX16 9AS

Tel	+44 (0)1398 331051
Email	thelodge@loyton.com
Web	www.loyton.com

Entry 50   Map 2

The Old Rectory Hotel Exmoor

A gorgeous small hotel in the hills above the Exmoor coast. The road from Lynton is a great way in, through woods that cling to a hill with the sea below. As for the Old Rectory, it's a mini Gidleigh Park, charming from top to toe. Three acres of spectacular gardens wrap around you, only birdsong disturbs you, though Exmoor deer occasionally come to drink from the pond. Inside, Huw and Sam continue to lavish love and money in all the right places. Their most recent addition is a beautiful orangery with smart sofas, warm colours and doors onto the garden for afternoon tea in the sun. Interiors are lovely: Farrow & Ball colours, the odd stone wall, a cute little sitting room, fresh flowers and books everywhere. Bedrooms are just as good with big beds, crisp linen, cool colours and beautiful bathrooms. You'll find digital radios, flat-screen TVs and the odd leather sofa, too. Spin into the restaurant for an excellent meal, perhaps Ilfracombe crab, Exmoor duck, strawberry champagne trifle. Afternoon tea 'on the house' is served in the garden in good weather.

Rooms	3 doubles, 4 twin/doubles: £205–£245.
	4 suites for 2: £260–£275.
	Price includes dinner for 2.
Meals	Dinner, 4 courses, included;
	non-residents £35.
Closed	November – March.

Huw Rees & Sam Prosser
The Old Rectory Hotel Exmoor
Martinhoe, Parracombe,
Barnstable, EX31 4QT

Tel	+44 (0)1598 763368
Email	info@oldrectoryhotel.co.uk
Web	www.oldrectoryhotel.co.uk

Northcote Manor

A small country-house hotel built on the site of a 15th-century monastery. Those who want peace in deep country will find it here. You wind up a one-mile drive, through a wood that bursts with colour in spring, then emerge onto a lush plateau of rolling hills; the view from the croquet lawn drifts east for ten miles. As for the house, wisteria wanders along old stone walls, while the odd open fire smoulders within. There's an airy hall that doubles as the bar, a country-house drawing room that floods with light, and a sitting room where you gather for pre-dinner drinks. Super food waits in a lovely dining room, steps lead down to a pretty conservatory, doors open onto a gravelled terrace for summer breakfasts with lovely views. Bedrooms are no less appealing – more traditional in the main house, more contemporary in the garden rooms. Expect padded bedheads, mahogany dressers, flat-screen TVs, silky throws. You can walk your socks off, then come home for a good meal, perhaps Cornish crab, local lamb, strawberry soufflé with vanilla ice-cream. Exmoor and North Devon's coasts are close.

Rooms	9 twin/doubles: £170–£280. 7 suites for 2: £170–£280. Singles from £120. Dinner, B&B from £130 per person. Extra bed/sofabed £15–£25 per person per night.
Meals	Light dishes from £6.50. Lunch £22.50–£25.50. Dinner, 3 courses, £45. Tasting menu £90. Sunday lunch from £28.50.
Closed	Never.

Richie Herkes
Northcote Manor
Burrington,
Umberleigh, EX37 9LZ

Tel   +44 (0)1769 560501
Email   rest@northcotemanor.co.uk
Web   www.northcotemanor.co.uk

The Lamb Inn

This 16th-century inn is adored by locals and visitors alike. It's a proper inn in the old tradition with gorgeous rooms and the odd touch of scruffiness to add authenticity to its earthy bones. It stands on a cobbled walkway in a village lost down tiny lanes, and those lucky enough to chance upon it leave reluctantly. Inside there are beams, but they are not sandblasted, red carpets with a little swirl, sofas in front of an open fire. Boarded menus trumpet irresistible food – carrot and orange soup, haunch of venison with a port jus, an excellent rhubarb crumble. You can eat wherever you want: in the bar, in the fancy restaurant, or out in the walled garden in good weather. There's a cobbled terrace, a skittle alley, maps for walkers and well-kept ales. Upstairs, seven rooms have a chic country style. Two have baths in the room, those in the barn have painted stone walls, the suite has a wood-burner and a private terrace. All are lovely with comfy beds, white linen, good power showers and flat-screen TVs. Kind staff chat with ease. Dartmoor waits, but you may well linger. Brilliant.

Rooms	5 doubles, 1 twin/double: £95–£130. 1 suite for 3: £145–£170. Singles £69. Extra bed/sofabed £19 p.p. per night.
Meals	Lunch from £9. Dinner, 3 courses, £20–£30. Sunday lunch from £11.95.
Closed	Rarely.

Nick Silk
The Lamb Inn
Sandford, EX17 4LW

Tel	+44 (0)1363 773676
Email	thelambinn@gmail.com
Web	www.lambinnsandford.co.uk

Mill End

Order a hearty packed lunch the night before, and set off on the Two Moors Way. This is a walkers' hotel run by generous people in a glorious patch of Dartmoor. Tara and Nick give you cream teas, maps of walks straight from the door, high tea for children, and a boot room for you and your muddy things – including the dog. Outside the river Teign runs alongside the gardens (yes, you can fish; there's even an in-house fly fishing school if you want to learn how) and homemade scones with clotted cream and jam are served in the sunshine. Inside are three dapper lounges where fires crackle and burn on chilly days. Order your gin and tonic, play a game of Scrabble then step into the restaurant for fresh fish, locally reared meats and gorgeous West Country cheeses. Bedrooms – some with garden views, others with French windows opening onto the lawns – are all a good size and have comfortable armchairs or sofas if you'd rather stay private. *Minimum stay: 2 nights on weekdays.*

Rooms	15 twin/doubles: £105–£200. 6 suites for 2: £190–£260. Singles from £80. Extra beds from £25.
Meals	Lunch from £6. Dinner, 3 courses, £30–£40. Sunday lunch £22–£26. Afternoon tea £18.95.
Closed	Never.

Tara & Nick Culverhouse
Mill End
Chagford, Newton Abbot, TQ13 8JN

Tel	+44 (0)1647 432282
Email	info@millendhotel.com
Web	www.millendhotel.com

Lewtrenchard Manor

A Jacobean mansion where the full aristocratic Monty is on display; *Onward Christian Soldiers* was written in the library. Although grand, with its spectacular hall, cavernous fireplace and dazzling ballroom, it's not stuffy and the Murray family run their hotel with friendly ease. Dogs are welcome here and walks shoot off in all directions. You can hire bikes nearby and explore the Camel Trail; the local Arundell Arms has fishing rights on the river Tamar and offers courses. Return for one of the hotel's relaxation therapies and an elegant afternoon tea. The silver service dinners come with vegetables from the walled garden. You can walk it off in the gardens: Gertrude Jekyll parterre, fountains, woodland and an avenue of beeches straight out of Thomas Hardy. The Dartmoor National Park can be reached on foot if you're feeling hearty. *Minimum stay: 2 nights at weekends. Pets by arrangement.*

Rooms	4 doubles, 6 twin/doubles: £180-£320. 4 suites for 2: £235-£340.
Meals	Lunch, bar meals from £5.95; restaurant from £21. Dinner, 3 courses, £49.50. Children over seven welcome in restaurant.
Closed	Never.

Sue, James, Duncan & Joan Murray
Lewtrenchard Manor
Lewdown,
Okehampton, EX20 4PN

Tel	+44 (0)1566 783222
Email	info@lewtrenchard.co.uk
Web	www.lewtrenchard.co.uk

The Horn of Plenty

The Horn of Plenty is one of those clever hotels that has survived the test of time by constantly improving itself. This latest addition is six gorgeous new rooms, four of which have terraces or balconies that give 40-mile views over the Tamar Valley. Potter about outside and find six acres of gardens, then a path that leads down through bluebell woods to the river. Inside, beautiful simplicity abounds: stripped floors, gilt mirrors, fine art, fresh flowers everywhere. Bedrooms in the main house come in country-house style, those in the garden have a contemporary feel. All have smart colours, big comfy beds, perhaps a claw-foot bath or a ceiling open to the rafters; ten have a terrace or a balcony. Despite all this, the food remains the big draw, so come to eat well, perhaps beetroot mousse with goat's cheese parfait, grilled duck with chicory and orange, chocolate cannelloni with banana sorbet; views of the Tamar snaking through the hills are included in the price. Afternoon tea is served on the patio in summer. Tavistock, Dartmoor and the Eden Project are close.

Rooms	16 twin/doubles: £120–£265. Singles £110–£255. Dinner, B&B £100–£172 per person. Extra bed/sofabed £25 p.p. per night.
Meals	Lunch from £21. Dinner, 3 courses, £52.50. Tasting menu £70. Afternoon tea from £9.50.
Closed	Never.

Julie Leivers & Damien Pease
The Horn of Plenty
Gulworthy,
Tavistock, PL19 8JD

Tel	+44 (0)1822 832528
Email	enquiries@thehornofplenty.co.uk
Web	www.thehornofplenty.co.uk

Entry 56   Map 2

Glazebrook House Hotel

The front door at Glazebrook may well be a rip in the space-time continuum. Outside, English decorum reigns; inside, a wonderland for your senses waits. You don't really find a hotel, more a contemporary art installation that you get to live in for a day or two. It's a reinvention of a 19th-century collector's house and it overflows with pink flamingos, enormous chandeliers, ancient maps, a bust of the queen with a halo instead of a crown. There's a dinosaur in the library, a tasting room for whisky and wine, a red-marbled bar with sofas and armchairs, then doors onto a terrace for afternoon tea. Rooms come fully loaded: vast beds, the loveliest linen, cool design, quirky art. You get iPads, smart TVs and minibars 'on the house'. Black marble bathrooms are flawless, with walk-in showers, fluffy robes, perhaps a free-standing bath. Ambrosial food waits downstairs, maybe goat's cheese mousse, rack of lamb, hake with shellfish butter, chocolate delice with popcorn. Although the A38 passes nearby, there's only a distant hum when you're outside, so don't let that put you off visiting this exceptional hotel. Dartmoor waits.

Rooms	6 doubles, 1 twin: £229-£289. 1 single: £199.
Meals	Lunch from £7. Dinner, 3 courses, about £40; 5-course tasting menu £45; 8-course tasting menu £64. Afternoon tea £7-£15.
Closed	Rarely.

Pieter & Fran Hamman
Glazebrook House Hotel
South Brent, TQ10 9JE
Tel   +44 (0)1364 73322
Email   enquiries@glazebrookhouse.com
Web   www.glazebrookhouse.com

Plantation House

This lovely small hotel delivers what so many of us want: a warm welcome, lovely food, rooms that spoil us rotten. Downstairs, a fire smoulders in the sitting-room bar; upstairs, fine Georgian windows frame views of hill and forest. Stylish bedrooms are full of comforts. They come with excellent bathrooms, lovely beds, crisp linen and warm colours. You get padded bedheads, sound systems, bowls of fruit, white robes to pad about in. Back downstairs, you'll succumb to a pre-dinner drink – in front of the fire in the bar in winter, out on the pretty terrace in summer. As for Richard's food, it bursts with flavour, so expect to eat well, perhaps Thai-style sea bass with ginger and lemongrass, local lamb with a Merlot jus, chocolate terrine with hazelnut ice cream. Soft fruits, vegetables and potatoes come from the garden in summer, as do home-laid eggs at breakfast. The river Erme passes across the road – follow it down to the sea and discover wonderful Wonwell Beach. There's lots to see around you: Dartmoor to the north, Totnes, Dartmouth, Salcombe and Slapton Sands to the south. Brilliant.

Rooms	5 doubles, 1 twin: £125–£185. 1 suite for 2: £195–£230. 1 single: £75–£80.
Meals	Dinner, 5 courses, from £36.
Closed	Never.

Richard Hendey
Plantation House
Totnes Road, Ermington,
Ivybridge, PL21 9NS

Tel	+44 (0)1548 831100
Email	info@plantationhousehotel.co.uk
Web	www.plantationhousehotel.co.uk

Burgh Island Hotel

When the tide is in this ocean liner of a hotel is stranded on its own island. It's romantic here and filled with history so allow yourself to be whisked back to the pre-war days of Agatha Christie and Noël Coward – both of whom were regular guests. Walk the coastline or spend idle days on the beach; there's a private cove with turquoise waters – a natural salt water swimming pool. Return to the terrace at the Palm Court Bar for afternoon tea or a cocktail with glorious sea views. You'll find a snooker room, table tennis and the library has TV. Dress up properly for three-course dinners in the Ballroom where there's usually a pianist or house band, although you can head for the Captain's Cabin or Ganges Restaurant if you prefer to be more casual. In the morning, tea or coffee is brought to your room – a nice old-fashioned touch. *Minimum stay: 2 nights at weekends.*

Rooms	10 doubles, 3 twin/doubles: £440-£510. 12 suites for 2: £570-£700. Price includes dinner for 2.
Meals	Lunch from £16. Dinner included; non-residents £75. Afternoon tea £18.50. Sunday lunch, non-residents, £62.
Closed	2-12 February.

The Reservations Team
Burgh Island Hotel
Burgh Island,
Bigbury-on-Sea, TQ7 4BG

Tel	+44 (0)1548 810514
Email	reception@burghisland.com
Web	www.burghisland.com

The Henley Hotel

A small house above the sea with fabulous views, super bedrooms and some of the loveliest food in Devon. Despite these credentials, it's Martyn and Petra who shine most brightly, their kind, generous approach making this a memorable place to stay. Warm interiors have wooden floors, Lloyd Loom furniture, the odd potted palm, then big windows to frame the view. Below, the Avon estuary slips gracefully out to sea. At high tide surfers ride the waves, at low tide you can walk on the sands. There's a pretty garden with a path tumbling down to the beach, binoculars in each room, a wood-burner in the snug and good books everywhere. Bedrooms are a steal (one is huge). Expect warm colours, crisp linen, tongue-and-groove panelling and robes in super little bathrooms. As for Martyn's table d'hôte dinners, expect to eat very well. Fish comes daily from Kingsbridge market, you might find grilled figs with goat's cheese and Parma ham, roast monkfish with a lobster sauce, then hot chocolate soufflé with fresh raspberries. Gorgeous Devon is all around. Better than the Ritz! *German spoken. Minimum stay: 2 nights at weekends.*

Rooms	2 doubles, 2 twin/doubles: £120-£137. 1 suite for 2: £150. Singles from £85. Dinner, B&B £87-£97 per person, 2 night minimum.
Meals	Dinner £36.
Closed	November – March.

Martyn Scarterfield & Petra Lampe
The Henley Hotel
Folly Hill, Bigbury-on-Sea,
Kingsbridge, TQ7 4AR

Tel   +44 (0)1548 810240
Email   thehenleyhotel@btconnect.com
Web   www.thehenleyhotel.co.uk

South Sands Hotel

Two coves west from the bustle of town, this smart hotel stands above the beach with views of water, hill and sky. Interiors have a New England feel — seaside colours, softly painted wood, walls of glass that bring in the view. Doors in the restaurant open onto a decked terrace; at high tide the beach disappears and the sea laps against the wall below. Pull yourself away to walk in the hills, sail on the water, hire a kayak or try your hand at paddle boarding. If that sounds too energetic, then drop down to the beach for family fun. Children are very welcome and you'll find beach towels, buckets and spades, even crabbing nets. Back at the hotel, you dine on lovely local food, perhaps Salcombe crab cakes with foraged leaves, moorland beef with a red wine sauce, chocolate fondant with pistachio ice cream. Rooms at the front have watery views, a couple have terraces, all have comfy beds, a smart style and swish bathrooms. One has 'his and hers' claw-foot baths that look out to sea, while the family suites have kitchens and separate bedrooms for kids. Brilliant. *Minimum stay: 2 nights at weekends.*

Rooms	16 doubles, 6 twin/doubles: £215–£395. 5 suites for 4: £595.
Meals	Lunch from £17.95. Dinner £15.95–£40.
Closed	Rarely.

Antoine Gay
South Sands Hotel
Bolt Head, Salcombe, TQ8 8LL
Tel   +44 (0)1548 859000
Email   enquiries@southsands.com
Web   www.southsands.com

Bayards Cove Inn

In 1620 the Mayflower stopped in Bayards Cove before sailing for America. It docked just outside this cool little inn, one of the oldest buildings in Dartmouth. But if its timber frames are ancient, then its jaunty interiors are the polar opposite with a warm contemporary feel that spreads itself far and wide. Once inside you realise you're in a small and quirky café/restaurant that does a good line in world wines and local ale. You also realise you've landed in heaven and soon you're planning an invasion of one of the bay windows, where you can sink into comfy armchairs and survey life inside and out. Interiors have warm colours, low beams, white stone walls and ancient wood everywhere. There are fairy lights, too, a bar weighted down by freshly baked cakes, and cool tunes afloat in the air. Cosy rooms have timber frames, padded bedheads, pretty fabrics, comfy beds. Most have compact shower rooms, but you won't mind for a minute; some have views of the water or wildly wonky floors. There's great food, perhaps crispy squid, moules frites, local ice creams. Dartmouth waits at the front door. *Minimum stay: 2 nights at weekends. Pets by arrangement.*

Rooms	4 doubles, 1 twin/double: £90–£155. 1 suite for 2: £130–£180. 1 family room for 4: £110–£160. Singles from £95..
Meals	Lunch from £5.95. Dinner from £9.95; not Mon–Wed off season.
Closed	Never.

Charlie & Zuzana Deuchar
Bayards Cove Inn
Lower Street, Dartmouth, TQ6 9AN

Tel	+44 (0)1803 839278
Email	info@bayardscoveinn.co.uk
Web	www.bayardscoveinn.co.uk

The Cary Arms at Babbacombe Bay

The Cary Arms is a chic little inn that hovers above Babbacombe Bay with views of sea and sky. But it's not like other inns. Its determination to spend money creating the lap of luxury is matchless. This explains the spectacular new suites and beach huts that have recently taken root in the garden. Walls of glass frame the view, bedrooms look out to sea, bathrooms with walk-in showers are hard to beat. Best of all is your terrace, metres from crystal clear waters, with views that stretch for miles. Don't expect to move too far, though the small spa with treatment rooms and a hydrotherapy pool is hard to resist. As for the inn, you can eat fresh seafood on terraces that drop downhill towards a small jetty where locals fish. The pub has six moorings in the bay, you can charter a boat and explore the coast or hire kayaks for fun on the water. Inside, you find stone walls, wooden floors and a fire that burns every day. Rooms in the house have a New England style, all but one with a private terrace or balcony. Excellent bathrooms come as standard, one has a claw-foot bath that looks out to sea. *Minimum stay: 2 nights in cottages.*

Rooms	7 doubles: £195–£295. 1 suite for 4, 9 suites for 2: £375–£475. 1 family room for 4: £395. 1 cottage for 6; 1 cottage for 8; 1 cottage for 9: from £550; £2,750–£3,250 per week. Extra bed/sofabed £25 p.p. per night. Dogs £20 per night.
Meals	Lunch from £7.95. Dinner £25–£35.
Closed	Never.

David Adams
The Cary Arms at Babbacombe Bay
Beach Road, Babbacombe,
Torquay, TQ1 3LX

Tel	+44 (0)1803 327110
Email	enquiries@caryarms.co.uk
Web	www.caryarms.co.uk

Southernhay House

A beautiful small hotel on the loveliest square in town, a short stroll from the cathedral. The house dates to 1805 and was built for a major returning from the Raj. These days, it mixes quirky design with all the comforts you'd expect of a small, city hotel. It's central, welcoming, the rooms are lovely, the dining room serves great bistro food and there's a chic bar for cocktails or a pint of local ale. Downstairs, French windows at the back of the house draw you onto a small terrace, where you can eat in good weather, perhaps mussels in a white wine sauce, bangers and mash with a rich gravy, chocolate fondant with vanilla ice cream. Potter about and find electric blue sofas, 50s starlets framed on the wall, old style radiators and beautiful art. Stylish bedrooms wait upstairs – some are bigger, all are lovely. Expect bold colours, sumptuous fabrics, Indian art, hi-tech gadgetry. Cool bathrooms come as standard, bigger rooms have free-standing baths. Exeter has lots to offer: Roman walls, a 12th-century cathedral, the imperious Royal Albert Memorial Museum & Art Gallery. Topsham is close for river walks. *Over 12s welcome.*

Rooms	10 doubles: £100–£288.
Meals	Breakfast £14. Lunch from £6.50.
	Dinner, 3 courses, about £30.
Closed	Rarely.

Deborah Clark & Tony Orchard
Southernhay House
36 Southernhay East,
Exeter, EX1 1NX

Tel	+44 (0)1392 435324
Email	home@southernhayhouse.com
Web	www.southernhayhouse.com

Sidmouth Harbour Hotel

This lovely spa hotel sits above the town with huge views across Lyme Bay towards Portland Bill. It's a great spot with a terrace that has addictive qualities when the sun shines and a beautiful restaurant with walls of glass to weatherproof the view. You're 200m away from two sandy beaches, perfect for sunny days, but the hotel has lots to stop you wandering: a couple of swimming pools, five treatment rooms, a steam room and a sauna. Potter about and find a white marble bar, coastal art in the airy sitting room, then a stylish restaurant, where a vast Chesterfield sofa runs along six tables. Bedrooms are scattered about, some in the main house, others in the courtyard, but all have the same cool style: seaside colours, blond wood furniture, robes for excellent bathrooms, padded headboards and crisp white linen. Several in the main house have sea views, some have balconies, too. By day you take to the coastal path, spin down to the town, or bask on the beach. By night you return for a slap-up meal; start with crab chowder, follow with roast chicken and top it all off with chocolate tart and vanilla ice cream. *Minimum stay: 2 nights at weekends April – October.*

Rooms	48 twin/doubles: £170–£350. 7 singles: £105–£185. Price includes dinner for 2.
Meals	Lunch from £6.50. Dinner, 3 courses, included; non-residents about £30. Afternoon tea from £16.50. Sunday lunch from £17.95.
Closed	Never.

Ken Cumming
Sidmouth Harbour Hotel
The Westcliff, Manor Road,
Sidmouth, EX10 8RU

Tel	+44 (0)1395 513252
Email	sidmouth@harbourhotels.co.uk
Web	www.sidmouth-harbour-hotel.co.uk

Alexandra Hotel & Restaurant

This chic hotel has rather good views, a clean sweep up the Jurassic coast all the way to Chesil Beach and on to Portland Bill. It sits high on the hill with one foot in town and the other paddling in the water. Directly below, the Cobb curls into the sea, the very spot where Meryl Streep withstood crashing waves in *The French Lieutenant's Woman*. Outside, there's a sun-trapping garden, where guests fall asleep in deckchairs, then a lookout tower with big sea views for a romantic dinner for two. Inside, an easy elegance flows: stripped wood floors, windows everywhere, an airy bar for pre-dinner drinks, an attractive sitting room with lots of books. There's a smart dining room that could double as a ballroom, then a conservatory brasserie that opens onto a terrace for lunch in summer. Both offer tasty, local food, perhaps Lyme Bay scallops, chicken with cavolo nero, a white chocolate mousse. Bedrooms, most with sea views, have warm colours, comfy beds, padded headboards, robes in fine bathrooms. Lyme, the beach, and the fossil-ridden coast, all wait. There's an 18th-century chapel, too. *Pets by arrangement*.

Rooms	18 twin/doubles: £180–£390. 3 family rooms for 4: £308–£480. 1 single: £95–£130. 1 apartment for 4, 1 apartment for 6: £315–£365
Meals	Lunch from £9.90. Dinner, 3 courses, about £35. Sunday lunch from £23. Afternoon tea from £7.50.
Closed	31 December – 31 January.

	Reservations Team
	Alexandra Hotel & Restaurant
	Pound Street,
	Lyme Regis, DT7 3HZ
Tel	+44 (0)1297 442010
Email	enquiries@hotelalexandra.co.uk
Web	www.hotelalexandra.co.uk

The Bull Hotel

The Bull was Dorset's first boutique hotel, a cool little place with lovely staff, an informal vibe, tasty food and lots of colour. It was bought by Fullers in 2014, who immediately poured in a small fortune to make it even better. The results are dreamy – airy interiors, big art, some fancy new bathrooms and a chic new restaurant. It remains as friendly as ever and draws a local crowd, who come for coffee and cake, a cool bar that rocks at weekends, even a masked ball on New Year's Eve. All of which makes it a lot of fun for guests passing through. Downstairs, you'll find an open fire, stripped wood floors and a pint of London Pride in the bar; in summer, life decants onto a flower-filled courtyard. Colourful bedrooms – all different – have lots of style: beautiful beds, pashmina throws, chic wallpapers, perhaps a bath at the foot of your bed. Some have sofas, family rooms have bunk beds for kids. You get digital radios, flat-screen TVs, then cool bathrooms, some with big power showers. Don't miss the food, perhaps Portland crab, Dorset lamb, coconut panna cotta. Chesil Beach is close. *Minimum stay: 2 nights at weekends.*

Rooms	10 doubles, 1 twin, 3 four-posters: £100-£230. 1 suite for 2: £235-£265. 3 family rooms for 4: £220-£260. 1 single: £90-£130.
Meals	Lunch, 2 courses, from £12. Dinner, 3 courses, around £35. Sunday lunch £13.50-£14.50.
Closed	Never.

Sian Thompson
The Bull Hotel
34 East Street,
Bridport, DT6 3LF

Tel	+44 (0)1308 422878
Email	info@thebullhotel.co.uk
Web	www.thebullhotel.co.uk

The Seaside Boarding House, Restaurant & Bar

You pop up the hill, come to the end of the road, then follow a track along the cliff and down to this lovely and bright small hotel. Rolling hills shoot north towards Dorchester, while the view east follows Chesil Beach, a mere 20 miles round to Portland Bill. The Boarding House's natural beauty comes courtesy of a recent facelift, proving conclusively that cosmetic surgery works. Outside, there's a dining terrace overlooking the sea, then paths that drop down to the beach. Inside, walls of glass flood big rooms with seaside light. There's a bar for cocktails and afternoon tea, a library with books and games for rainy days, then a restaurant for delicious food: perhaps cheese soufflé, whole lemon sole and chocolate and hazelnut delice. Upstairs bedrooms all have sea views and mix period furniture (some from HMS Windsor) with 21st-century design: beautiful beds, Zoffany colours, rugs on wood floors, cushioned window seats. Bathrooms have white robes and vintage tiles, then a big shower, a claw-foot bath, or both. The coastal path passes directly outside, so bring your boots. Brilliant. *Minimum stay: 2 nights at weekends.*

Rooms	9 doubles: £180–£235.
Meals	Lunch from £14. Dinner, 3 courses, about £30. Sunday lunch £25–£30. Afternoon tea from £10.
Closed	Never.

Mary-Lou Sturridge
The Seaside Boarding House,
Restaurant & Bar
Cliff Road, Burton Bradstock, DT6 4RB

Tel	+44 (0)1308 897205
Email	info@theseasideboardinghouse.com
Web	theseasideboardinghouse.com

Bridge House Hotel

Beaminster – or Emminster in Thomas Hardy's *Tess* – sits in a lush Dorset valley. From the hills above, you drop through glorious country, rolling down to this old market town, where the church tower soars towards heaven. As for this lovely hotel, it's a 13th-century priest's house and comes with original trimmings: stone flags, mullioned windows, old beams and huge inglenooks. It's intimate, friendly and deeply comfortable, with something beautiful at every turn. There are rugs on parquet flooring, a beamed bar with an open fire, a splendid dining room with Georgian panelling and a Robert Adam's fireplace. Beautiful lighting sets the mood for excellent food, perhaps Witchampton snails, an imperious steak and kidney pie, pear and rosemary tarte tatin. Rooms in the main house are bigger and smarter, those in the coach house are simpler and less expensive; all are pretty with chic fabrics, crisp linen, flat-screen TVs and stylish bathrooms. Breakfast is served in the conservatory, so watch the gardener potter about as you scoff your bacon and eggs. Chesil Beach at West Bay is close. *Minimum stay: 2 nights at weekends.*

Rooms	6 doubles, 3 twin/doubles, 2 four-posters: £99–£260. 2 family rooms for 4: £99–£260. Dinner, B&B £82.50–£145 p.p. (obligatory on Fridays & Saturdays from April to September). Extra beds: children under 17 £25; adults £35–£50.
Meals	Lunch from £8.50. Dinner, 3 courses, £25–£35.
Closed	Never.

Chris Staines
Bridge House Hotel
3 Prout Bridge,
Beaminster, DT8 3AY

Tel	+44 (0)1308 862200
Email	enquiries@bridge-house.co.uk
Web	www.bridge-house.co.uk

The Greyhound

It's hard to fault this little inn. It sits in one of Dorset's loveliest villages, lost in a lush valley with country views that shoot uphill. Outside, there's a colourful terrace that draws a crowd in summer. Inside, cool, rustic interiors mix old and new to great effect. You find stone walls, old flagstones, gilt mirrors and a wood-burner to keep things cosy. There's a lively locals' bar where you can grab a pint of real ale, then a cosy little restaurant where you dig into delicious food. The feel throughout is informal and you can eat wherever you want, so spin onto the terrace in good weather and try seared scallops, boeuf bourguignon, sticky toffee pudding. Six lovely rooms wait in an old skittle alley. They're not huge, but nor is their price, and what they lack in space, they make up for in comfort and style, with crisp linen, airy colours and pretty furniture. There's a DVD library, too, and wellington boots if you want to walk. The Cerne Abbas giant is close, while the coast is on your doorstep: Lyme Regis for fossil hunters, West Bay for fine walking and fabulous Chesil Beach. *Minimum stay: 2 nights on bank holidays.*

Rooms	5 doubles, 1 twin: £89–£99. Singles from £69.
Meals	Lunch from £5.50. Dinner, 3 courses, about £30; not Sunday.
Closed	Rarely.

Matthew Martinez
The Greyhound
26 High Street, Sydling St Nicholas,
Dorchester, DT2 9PD

Tel	+44 (0)1300 341303
Email	info@dorsetgreyhound.co.uk
Web	www.dorsetgreyhound.co.uk

Entry 70   Map 2

The Priory Hotel

The lawns of this 16th-century priory run down to the river Frome. Boats float past, an old church rises behind, a gorgeous garden filled with colour wraps around you. As for this lovely country house, you'll find a grand piano in the drawing room, a first-floor sitting room with garden views, then a new restaurant with walls of glass that juts into the garden giving rather good views. There's a beautiful terrace, too, where you can sit in the sun and watch the river pass. Bedrooms in the main house come in different sizes, some cosy in the eaves, others grandly adorned in reds and golds. You get Zoffany fabrics, padded window seats, bowls of fruit, the odd sofa. Eight have river views, others look onto the garden or church. Chic bathrooms – some dazzlingly contemporary – all come with white robes. Rooms in the boathouse, a 16th-century clay barn, are lavish, with oak panelling, stone walls and sublime views. Outside, climbing roses, a duck pond, banks of daffs and snowdrops in spring. Corfe Castle and Studland Bay are close. A slice of old England with delicious food to boot. *Minimum stay: 2 nights at weekends. Over 14s welcome.*

Rooms	12 twin/doubles: £220–£320.
	5 suites for 2: £350–£380.
Meals	Lunch from £14.95.
	Dinner, 3 courses, £47.50.
Closed	Never.

Jeremy Merchant
The Priory Hotel
Church Green,
Wareham, BH20 4ND

Tel	+44 (0)1929 551666
Email	reservations@theprioryhotel.co.uk
Web	theprioryhotel.co.uk

Urban Beach Hotel

A quirky little place with surfer-chic interiors, lovely staff and a happy buzz throughout. You're on a residential street 500 metres back from the beach; a short stroll leads down to the promenade which you can follow into town. Back at the hotel a relaxed informality reigns. You'll find circular leather booths, driftwood lamps, a house guitar and surf boards hanging on the wall. There's a bar for cocktails, candle lanterns scattered about, a table laden with cakes, then the daily papers and cool tunes in the air. Outside, a terrace for all seasons waits, with a roof that disappears when the sun shines and a fire pit for cooler nights. Bedrooms upstairs come in different sizes, but even the smaller rooms are lovely with warm colours, crisp linen and smart bathrooms. The beach waits at the end of the road, seven miles of sand with a surf shop on the way down. Come back for a good meal, perhaps cauliflower soup, Cornish mussels, a melting chocolate fondant. Urban Reef, Mark & Fiona's sister restaurant, has a balcony and terrace overlooking the sea, not a bad spot for dinner in summer. *Minimum stay: 2 nights at weekends; 3 nights over bank holidays.*

Rooms	9 doubles, 1 twin/double: £89-£180. 2 singles: £72.
Meals	Lunch from £6. Dinner £25-30. Sunday lunch from £14.
Closed	Never.

Mark & Fiona Cribb
Urban Beach Hotel
23 Argyll Road,
Bournemouth, BH5 1EB
Tel   +44 (0)1202 301509
Email   reception@urbanbeach.co.uk
Web   www.urbanbeach.co.uk

Captain's Club Hotel and Spa

The Captain's Club stands on the banks on the Stour, where a tiny ferry potters along the river dodging swans and ducks. In summer, you decant onto its lovely terrace and watch river life pass by. Inside, walls of glass weatherproof the view. The sprawling bar fills with light and comes with deep sofas, the daily papers and a grand piano. It's smart, stylish and very informal, with live music at weekends. The hotel also has its own boat, so you can take to the high seas and spin over to the Isle of Wight or Brownsea Island. Back on dry land uncluttered bedrooms have river views, low-slung beds, crisp white linen, neutral colours and excellent bathrooms. None are small, some are huge with separate sitting rooms, apartments have more than one bedroom, so perfect for families and friends. There's a spa, too, with a hydrotherapy pool, a sauna and four treatment rooms. Lovely food is on tap all day in the bar, while the mirrored restaurant ensures everyone has the view. Lobster, Dorset crab, sea bass and a good steak all wait. Christchurch is a short walk upstream. Brilliant. *Minimum stay: 2 nights at weekends.*

Rooms	17 doubles: £199–£259.
	12 apartments for 6: £289–£649.
Meals	Bar meals all day from £6.
	Lunch from £15. Dinner £30–£35.
Closed	Never.

Timothy Lloyd & Robert Wilson
Captain's Club Hotel and Spa
Wick Ferry,
Christchurch, BH23 1HU

Tel	+44 (0)1202 475111
Email	reservations@captainsclubhotel.com
Web	www.captainsclubhotel.com

The Kings

This is one of those lovely places that delivers what many of us want: lots of style, delicious food, happy staff, attractive prices. The setting is just as good, a slice of Georgian England, with the river Stour to the left, the ruined castle to the right and the old bowling green in between. A riverside path leads down to Christchurch Quay, and another to the gardens at the priory – blissful stuff. As for the hotel, you'll find a cool new bar with big orange armchairs, green leather bar stools and candles everywhere at night – not a bad spot for champagne cocktails. Comfy bedrooms have lots of style: smart colours, fine beds, good bathrooms, perhaps a sofa if there's room. Three overlook the front, those in the eaves have a cute, cosy feel. Back downstairs you find the big draw – excellent food in the candlelit restaurant. Try Dorset cheddar soufflé, turbot with garlic and thyme, lemon meringues with limoncello. It's all local with menus from an amazing £15. Lobster nights bring in the locals, the Christchurch Food Festival comes in May with stalls on the bowling green. Perfect. *Minimum stay: 2 nights at weekends.*

Rooms	18 doubles, 2 twins: £99–£199.
Meals	Lunch from £6.50. Dinner, 2 courses, from £15; à la carte about £30. Sunday lunch from £15. Afternoon tea £12.95
Closed	Never.

Lukasz Dwornik
The Kings
18 Castle Street,
Christchurch, BH23 1DT

Tel	+44 (0)1202 588933
Email	kings@harbourhotels.co.uk
Web	www.thekings-christchurch.co.uk

Castleman Hotel & Restaurant

It's a little like stepping into the pages of a Hardy novel: an untouched corner of rural Dorset, a 400-year-old bailiff's house, sheep grazing in lush fields, a rich cast of characters pottering about. The Castleman — part country house, part restaurant with rooms — is a true one-off: quirky, intimate, defiantly English (you'll think you've landed in Ambridge). It pays no heed to prevailing fashions, not least because the locals would revolt if it did. Barbara runs the place in great style. Touches of grandeur are hard to miss: a panelled hall, art from Chettle House, a magnificent Jacobean ceiling in one of the sitting rooms. Follow your nose and find a cosy bar, fresh flowers everywhere and books galore. The restaurant has garden views, though your eyes are more likely to be fixed on Barbara's delicious old-school food, perhaps potted shrimp terrine, haunch of local venison, meringues with chocolate mousse and toasted almonds. Homely bedrooms fit the bill: comfortable, delightfully priced, a couple with claw-foot baths. Magical Dorset will fill your days with splendour. Don't miss it.

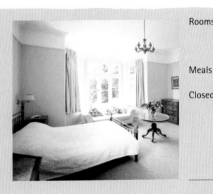

Rooms	4 doubles, 1 twin/double, 1 twin, 1 four-poster: £95–£110. 1 family room for 4: £95–£110. Singles from £70.
Meals	Dinner, 3 courses, about £27. Sunday lunch £25.
Closed	February.

Barbara Garnsworthy
Castleman Hotel & Restaurant
Chettle,
Blandford Forum, DT11 8DB

Tel	+44 (0)1258 830096
Email	enquiry@castlemanhotel.co.uk
Web	www.castlemanhotel.co.uk

Plumber Manor

Plumber is old school, it pays no heed to passing fashions, it just gets on with doing what it does so well – looking after guests, pouring fine libations, serving delicious food. It is suitably lost in Dorset's mazy lanes, a fine old pile of golden stone that dates to 1650. It sits in a couple of acres of green and pleasant land with the river Divelish flanking one side. Outside, there's a terrace for afternoon tea with beautiful magnolias on show in summer. Inside, a pair of labradors rule the roost. There's an open fire in the sitting-room bar, fresh flowers, old clocks, a snug in cherry red. The first-floor landing has an enormous sofa, a gallery of family portraits, a grand piano for good measure. Bedrooms are split between the main house and converted barns; the latter are big and welcome dogs. Décor is dated – 1980s florals – as are bathrooms, though several now sparkle in travertine splendour. A family triumvirate oversee it all: Brian in the kitchen, Richard behind the bar, Alison everywhere. Hearty food waits, perhaps crab mousseline, rack of lamb, lemon meringue pie.

Rooms	16 twin/doubles: £160-£240. Singles from £120.
Meals	Dinner £30-£38. Sunday lunch £30.
Closed	February.

Richard, Alison & Brian Prideaux-Brune
Plumber Manor
Plumber,
Sturminster Newton, DT10 2AF

Tel	+44 (0)1258 472507
Email	book@plumbermanor.com
Web	www.plumbermanor.com

The Grosvenor Arms

Shaftesbury, an ancient country seat, has seen its fair share of history. In 888 King Alfred founded an abbey here; in 1035 King Canute died within its walls. It is surrounded by flawless country, with Cranborne Chase rolling south for miles on end. By day you go in search of sweeping vistas, ancient woodlands, the odd prehistoric hill fort. By night you return to this cool inn to make merry. Inside, the sitting-room bar doubles as a café and acts as the hub of the inn; it's open all day and buzzes with local life, so sink into a sofa, grab the daily papers and while away the afternoon. Elsewhere, an airy restaurant for wood-fired pizzas and local steaks, then a conservatory that opens onto a courtyard in good weather. Bedrooms upstairs are just the ticket: none are small, some are huge, all have warm colours, big beds and sparkling bathrooms. One opens onto a balcony, one of the suites comes with a chaise longue, another has a claw-foot bath in the room; all have coffee machines, flat-screen TVs and posh oils. Gold Hill, a steep cobbled street around the corner, is famous for its timeless view. *Free passes for the car park across the road.*

Rooms	6 twin/doubles: £90-£160. 8 doubles: £95-£160. 2 suites for 2: £140-£180. Dogs £10 per night.
Meals	Lunch from £5.50. Dinner, 3 courses, £20-£35. Sunday lunch from £16.
Closed	Never.

Kirsty Schmidt
The Grosvenor Arms
The Commons,
Shaftesbury, SP7 8JA
Tel   +44 (0)1747 850 580
Email   k.schmidt@grosvenorarms.co.uk
Web   www.grosvenorarms.co.uk

Entry 77   Map 3

Rose & Crown

Romaldkirk is one of those lovely villages where little has changed in 200 years. It sits peacefully in the north Pennines, lost to the world and without great need of it. As for the Rose & Crown, it dates to 1733 and stands on the village green next to a Saxon church. Roses ramble across stone walls at the front, so grab a pint of local ale, then sit in the sun and watch life pass by. Inside, you can roast away in front of a fire in the wonderfully old-school bar while reading the *Teesdale Mercury*. There's a peaceful sitting room for afternoon tea, then a panelled restaurant for excellent food, perhaps honey-glazed goats cheese with apple and hazelnut, shoulder of pork wrapped in Parma ham, banana Bakewell tart. Thomas and Cheryl bought the place in 2012 and have been spending money on it ever since: it has never looked better. Stylish rooms – some in the main house, others out back, a couple in a cottage next door – have warm colours, comfy beds, Bose sound systems and super bathrooms. Don't miss High Force waterfall, the magnificent Bowes Museum or the sausage sandwich at lunch. Dogs are very welcome.

Rooms	7 doubles, 3 twins: £115-£160.
	2 suites for 2: £180-£200.
	1 cottage for 4: £115-£200. Singles £95.
	Dinner, B&B from £79 per person.
Meals	Lunch from £10.50. Dinner, 3 courses,
	from £27. Sunday lunch £19.50.
Closed	23-27 December; 1 week in January.

	Thomas & Cheryl Robinson
	Rose & Crown
	Romaldkirk,
	Barnard Castle, DL12 9EB
Tel	+44 (0)1833 650213
Email	hotel@rose-and-crown.co.uk
Web	www.rose-and-crown.co.uk

The Pier at Harwich

They don't do things by halves at the Pier – a cool £1.5 million has recently been spent on a 21st-century makeover for this iconic coastal hotel. It sits on the harbourside with views of town and water, its front terrace a big draw in good weather. Inside, a cool new look captivates. A chic warehouse feel waits in the bar – stripped walls, hanging lamps, leather bar stools, big windows to frame the view. You get craft beers and cask ales, a gin library and prosecco cocktails, then small plates of Nordic design if you fancy a light bite. Hungry souls fly upstairs to the famous first-floor brasserie, where mirrored booths and leather banquettes now come as standard, and doors open onto a balcony, where you can tuck into your lobster Thermidor while gazing out onto the estuary. Bedrooms – some above, others next door in a former inn – have fancy bedheads, seaside colours, crisp white linen and super bathrooms; the suite, with its vast window, has a telescope with which to scan the high seas. Coastal walks and blue flag beaches wait, as does the Electric Palace, the second oldest cinema in Britain.

Rooms	10 doubles, 3 twins: £120-£170. 1 suite for 2: £200-£230. Singles from £95. Dinner, B&B from £100 p.p.
Meals	Lunch from £6.50. Dinner à la carte £25-£40. Sunday lunch from £19.50.
Closed	Never.

Paul & Geraldine Milsom
The Pier at Harwich
The Quay,
Harwich, CO12 3HH

Tel	+44 (0)1255 241212
Email	pier@milsomhotels.com
Web	www.milsomhotels.com

The Mistley Thorn

This welcoming inn fits the Sawday bill perfectly – lovely owners with fingers dipped into delicious local pies. Their kitchen shop and cooking school stand four doors down the street; Lucca, their popular wood-fired pizzeria, waits in Manningtree. As for their inn, it stands on the high street and dates to 1746. Interiors have an airy feel, the mood is laid-back with a great little bar, the food is local and utterly delicious. Expect tongue-and-groove panelling, a roaring wood-burner, padded benches and a happy vibe. Nicely-priced rooms (two above the kitchen shop) have a similar feel: pretty fabrics, warm colours, crisp linen on comfy beds, REN lotions for power showers and double-ended baths. There's good art, homemade shortbread and fresh fruit, too, while those at the front have views of the Stour estuary. As for the food, it's delicious stuff, perhaps smoked haddock chowder, mussels with garlic and herbs, sticky toffee pudding. The Witchfinder General lived here, you can walk along the river to Dedham, the Beth Chatto Gardens are close.

Rooms	5 doubles, 3 twin/doubles: £110–£125. Singles from £90. Dinner, B&B from £75 per person.
Meals	Lunch from £4.95. Set lunch, 2–3 courses £12.50–£15. Dinner, 3 courses, about £30.
Closed	Rarely.

David McKay & Sherri Singleton
The Mistley Thorn
High Street, Mistley,
Manningtree, CO11 1HE
Tel   +44 (0)1206 392821
Email   info@mistleythorn.co.uk
Web   www.mistleythorn.co.uk

The Sun Inn

This perennial favourite sits in an idyllic village made rich by mills in the 16th century. You're also in Constable country – the artist attended school in the village and often returned to paint the church. Best of all is the river – you can hire boats, grab a picnic from the inn, float down the sleepy Stour, then tie up on the bank for lunch al fresco. As for The Sun, you couldn't hope to wash up in a better spot. Inside, you find open fires, boarded floors, timber frames and an easy elegance. A panelled lounge comes with sofas and armchairs, the bar is made from a slab of local elm and the airy, beamed dining room offers fabulous food inspired by Italy, perhaps crab ravioli, squid with chilli and garlic, monkfish with truffle mash, chocolate mousse with Morello cherries. Rooms are gorgeous: creaking floorboards, timber-framed walls, a panelled four-poster. Those at the back are bigger and come in grand style, but all are lovely with crisp linen, local art and power showers in excellent bathrooms. There's afternoon tea on arrival if you book in advance and a garden for a pint in summer. *Pets by arrangement.*

Rooms	5 doubles, 1 twin/double, 1 four-poster: £90–£145. Dinner, B&B £100–£125 p.p. Extra bed/sofabed available £15 p.p. per night.
Meals	Lunch from £10.95; not Mondays. Dinner from £16.95.
Closed	Christmas.

Piers Baker
The Sun Inn
High Street, Dedham,
Colchester, CO7 6DF

Tel	+44 (0)1206 323351
Email	office@thesuninndedham.com
Web	www.thesuninndedham.com

Maison Talbooth

The outdoor swimming pool is heated to 29°C every day, a chauffeur is on hand to whisk you down to the hotel's riverside restaurant, a grand piano waits in the sitting room, where guests gather for a legendary afternoon tea. They don't do things by halves at Maison Talbooth, a small-scale pleasure dome with long views across Constable country. The house, an old rectory, stands in three acres of manicured grounds; the pool house is a big draw with its open fire, honesty bar, beautiful art and treatment rooms. Interiors are equally impressive. There are no bedrooms, only suites, each divine; all pamper you rotten with flawless bathrooms, fabulous beds, cool colours and hi-tech excess. At dinner you're chauffeured to the family's restaurants (both within half a mile): Milsoms for bistro food served informally; Le Talbooth on the river Stour for more serious fare, perhaps poached lobster with orange and fennel, saddle of venison with plums and bitter chocolate, pineapple and coconut soufflé with piña colada ice cream. A great escape.

Rooms	12 suites for 4: £210–£420. Singles from £170.
Meals	Dinner at Milsoms £25; at Le Talbooth £35–£50.
Closed	Never.

Paul & Geraldine Milsom
Maison Talbooth
Stratford Road, Dedham,
Colchester, CO7 6HN

Tel	+44 (0)1206 322367
Email	maison@milsomhotels.com
Web	www.milsomhotels.com

The Wheatsheaf

The Wheatsheaf stands at the vanguard of a cool new movement: the village local reborn in country-house style. It's a winning formula with locals and travellers flocking in for a heady mix of laid-back informality and chic English style. The inn stands between pretty hills in this ancient wool village on the Fosse Way. Inside, happy young staff flit about, throwing logs on the fire, ferrying food to diners, or simply stopping for a chat. Downstairs, you find armchairs in front of smouldering fires, noble portraits on panelled walls, cool tunes playing in the background. Outside, a smart courtyard garden draws a crowd in summer, so much so it has its own bar; English ales, jugs of Pimm's and lovely wines all wait. Back inside, beautiful bedrooms come as standard, some bigger than others, all fully loaded with comfort and style. Expect period colours, Hypnos beds, Bang & Olufsen TVs, and spectacular bathrooms with beautiful baths and/or power showers. As for the food, you feast on lovely local fare, perhaps devilled kidneys, coq au vin, pear and almond tart. Don't miss it.

Rooms	14 doubles: £120–£180.
	Extra bed £25 child, £75 adult.
Meals	Lunch from £9. Dinner, 3 courses,
	about £30. Bar meals from £5.
Closed	Never.

Reservations
The Wheatsheaf
West End, Northleach,
Cheltenham, GL54 3EZ

Tel	+44 (0)1451 860244
Email	reservations@cotswoldswheatsheaf.com
Web	www.cotswoldswheatsheaf.com

Three Choirs Vineyards

England's answer to the Napa Valley. After 15 years of tilling the soil (very sandy, good drainage), Thomas's 75 acres of Gloucestershire hillside now produce 300,000 bottles a year. There are regular tastings, a shop in which to buy a bottle or two, and paths that weave through the vines – a perfect stroll after a good meal. What's more, three fabulous lodges wait down by the lake, all with decks and walls of glass. You'll find claw-foot baths and comfy beds, so camp out in grand savannah style and listen to the woodpeckers. Rooms up at the restaurant are smart and spacious with terraces that overlook the vineyard. They come with padded bedheads, walls of colour, leather armchairs, flat-screen TVs and good bathrooms. Finally, the restaurant: claret walls, lovely views, sofas in front of an open fire. Excellent food waits, perhaps twice-baked Gloucester soufflé, fillet of bream with rocket and watercress, rhubarb crème brûlée with lemon shortbread. World wines are on the list, but you'll want something from the vines that surround you; there's a microbrewery, too. Perfect. *Minimum stay: 2 nights at weekends.*

Rooms	6 doubles, 3 vineyard lodges, 2 twins: £153-£203. Singles from £135.
Meals	Lunch from £7.50. Dinner à la carte about £35.
Closed	Christmas & New Year.

Thomas Shaw
Three Choirs Vineyards
Castle Tump,
Newent, GL18 1LS

Tel	+44 (0)1531 890223
Email	info@threechoirs.com
Web	www.three-choirs-vineyards.co.uk

Tudor Farmhouse Hotel

A gorgeous small hotel, one of the best. It sits on the edge of the Forest of Dean, a magical world of woodland walks, medieval castles, meandering rivers and bleating sheep. You're in the middle of a tiny village with country views all around. Step inside to find sparkling interiors – Colin and Hari have spent a small fortune turning their realm into something very special indeed. An airy elegance mixes with golden stone walls and original timber frames, the house bearing testament to its Tudor roots. Big or small, bedrooms are divine – stylishly uncluttered with smart fabrics, robes in fine bathrooms and super-comfy beds. Those in the main house have ancient beamed ceilings, those in the old barns have original stone walls. The bigger rooms are faultless: the best beds, claw-foot baths, enormous showers, the lap of luxury. Lovely local food waits downstairs, perhaps cider-cured salmon, haunch of venison, rhubarb Bakewell tart; there are home-laid eggs for breakfast, too. You can kayak on the Wye, forage in the forest, take to cycle tracks. Don't miss Puzzlewood or Clearwell Caves. *Minimum stay: 2 nights at weekends.*

Rooms	10 doubles, 3 twins, 2 four-posters: £130–£250. 5 suites for 2: £220–£250. Singles £90–£220. Extra bed/sofabed £25 per person per night.
Meals	Lunch from £6.95. Dinner, 3 courses, £30–£40. Sunday lunch from £14.50.
Closed	Never.

Colin & Hari Fell
Tudor Farmhouse Hotel
High Street,
Clearwell, GL16 8JS
Tel   +44 (0)1594 833046
Email   info@tudorfarmhousehotel.co.uk
Web   www.tudorfarmhousehotel.co.uk

Chewton Glen

Chewton Glen is one of the loveliest country-house hotels in the land. It opened in 1964 with eight bedrooms, and even though it now has over 70, it remains delightfully intimate. 50 years of evolution have brought a pillared swimming pool, a hydrotherapy spa, a golf course and a tennis centre. The most recent addition is The Kitchen, an informal foil to the main restaurant, where you can also come for cookery classes. As for the hotel, expect beautiful sitting rooms, roaring fires, busts and oils, a bar that opens onto a sun-trapping terrace. Bedrooms mix country-house style with contemporary flair. Expect marble bathrooms, private balconies, designer fabrics, flawless housekeeping. You'll also find 13 treehouse suites that sit peacefully in their own valley with hot tubs on balconies and wood-burners within. Beyond, nine gardeners tend 130 acres of lawns and woodland, with a kitchen garden that serves both restaurants. The food is exceptional, perhaps twice-baked cheese soufflé, Thai lobster curry, pineapple and black pepper tarte tatin. Beach and forest wait, there's croquet on the lawn in summer. *Minimum stay: 2 nights at weekends.*

Rooms	5 doubles, 30 twin/doubles: £325-£695. 23 suites for 2: £800-£1495. 13 treehouses for 2: £850-£2850.
Meals	Breakfast £21-£26. The Kitchen: lunch & dinner from £10. Main restaurant: lunch, 3 courses, £26.50. Dinner, 3 courses, £50-£70. Tasting menu £70. Afternoon tea £29.50. Sunday lunch £39.50.
Closed	Never.

Andrew Stembridge
Chewton Glen
Christchurch Road,
New Milton, BH25 6QS

Tel	+44 (0)1425 275341
Email	reservations@chewtonglen.com
Web	www.chewtonglen.com

The Manor at Sway

A big house in a small village in the middle of the New Forest – lovely gardens run down to woodland, the odd deer comes in to nibble the roses. Inside, country-house interiors have a distinctly contemporary feel – airy and nicely stylish with wood floors, pretty wallpapers and a relaxed feel. You'll find smart sofas in the sitting room, then a chic bar with a wall of glass that opens onto the terrace, perfect for afternoon tea in the sun. Bedrooms are lovely. They come in different shapes and sizes, but all have the same comforts: excellent beds, crisp linen, warm colours, sparkling bathrooms. Three are dog-friendly, those in the eaves are warmly cosy, larger rooms have armchairs, most have garden views. The big surprise is the delicious food, so work up an appetite in the forest by day, then come home for a feast, perhaps scallops with curried cauliflower, local venison in a port sauce, Bakewell tart with blackberry jam. There are simpler dishes, too: posh fish and chips, pork belly with buttered greens, beetroot tarte tatin. Fabulous walking, mountain bike trails and sun loungers in the garden wait. *Minimum stay: 2 nights at weekends.*

Rooms	12 doubles, 3 twin/doubles: £90–£210.
Meals	Lunch from £6.
	Dinner, 3 courses, £30–£40.
	Sunday lunch £19.50–£24.50.
Closed	Rarely.

Tim Holloway
The Manor at Sway
Station Road, Sway,
Lymington, SO41 6BA

Tel	+44 (0)1590 682754
Email	info@swaymanor.com
Web	www.themanoratsway.com

Daisybank Cottage Boutique B&B

This chic B&B in the New Forest mixes a warm contemporary style with some fine, old-fashioned hospitality — Ciaran and Cheryl go out of their way to make your stay special. As for their lovely Arts & Crafts house, it sits peacefully on the southern fringes of Brockenhurst with pretty gardens front and back. There's a juke box in the breakfast room, an honesty bar for pre-dinner drinks and a relaxing reading room. Spoiling bedrooms have airy colours, plantation shutters, Vi-Spring mattresses on lovely beds, then robes in stylish bathrooms. One has a claw-foot bath, another at the back opens onto the garden; keep going you'll find a shepherd's hut with its own wood-burner and a small terrace. All rooms have coffee machines, silent fridges in which to chill drinks, iPod docks and flat-screen TVs. Breakfast is a feast: local eggs, artisan jams, home-baked soda bread, bacon and sausages from a local farm. You can walk by the sea or explore the forest by foot, bike or horse. Good restaurants wait in town (a gentle ten-minute stroll), perhaps Thai, French or an excellent pizza. *Minimum stay: 2 nights at weekends. Children over 8 welcome.*

Rooms	4 doubles: £110-£155. 2 cottages for 2; 1 shepherd's hut for 2: £110-£155. Extra bed/sofabed £35-£40 p.p.p.n.
Meals	Restaurants within half a mile.
Closed	One week over Christmas.

Cheryl & Ciaran Maher
Daisybank Cottage Boutique B&B
Sway Road,
Brockenhurst, SO42 7SG

Tel	+44 (0)1590 622086
Email	info@bedandbreakfast-newforest.co.uk
Web	www.bedandbreakfast-newforest.co.uk

The Montagu Arms

Beaulieu, an ancient royal hunting ground, was gifted to Cistercian monks by King John in 1204. Their abbey took 40 years to build and you can visit its ruins in the nearby grounds of Palace House, seat of the Montagu family since 1538. As for the village, its tiny high street is a hotchpotch of 17th-century timber-framed houses that totter by the tidal estuary drinking in the view. The hotel dates to 1742, but was re-modelled in 1925, giving interiors an Arts & Crafts country-house feel. You'll find roaring fires and deep sofas, then a library bar and a courtyard garden where you can eat in summer. Chic bedrooms come with period furniture, smart fabrics, fresh flowers and robes in spotless bathrooms. Downstairs, ambrosial food is the big draw, perhaps truffle risotto with wild mushrooms, saddle of roe deer with parsnip purée, Seville orange soufflé with pepper ice-cream. There's a gastro pub if you want something simpler: local fish pie, ham and chips with poached eggs from resident hens. A kitchen garden provides much for the table, too. Beautiful walks start from the front door. *Minimum stay: 2 nights at weekends.*

Rooms	12 doubles, 1 twin, 4 four-posters: £157–£317. 7 suites for 2: £257–£377. Singles from £129. Dinner, B&B from £140 per person.
Meals	Lunch, 3 courses, from £25. Dinner from £18; tasting menu, 7 courses, £90. Sunday lunch from £32.50.
Closed	Never.

Andrew Nightingale
The Montagu Arms
Palace Lane, Beaulieu,
Brockenhurst, SO42 7ZL

Tel	+44 (0)1590 612324
Email	reservations@montaguarmshotel.co.uk
Web	www.montaguarmshotel.co.uk

The Master Builder's House Hotel

The position here is hard to beat: lawns run down to the river, yacht masts flutter in the breeze, ancient woodland runs along the water, soundproofing this beautiful landscape. As for the house, it dates to 1729 and was home to the shipwrights who built Nelson's fleet; several ships built here saw action at Trafalgar. These days peace reigns. A chic sitting room opens onto a smart garden, where gravel paths weave past colourful beds to tables for lunch in the sun. There's a lovely old bar and an airy restaurant – both have terraces that drink in the view, and both serve tasty local fare, too, perhaps a pizza or posh fish and chips in the bar; smoked rabbit chorizo, pot au feu with local veg, salted butterscotch crème brûlée in the restaurant. Bedrooms in the main house have big views, Indian furniture, then colour and character in spades. Those in the annexe, recently refurbished (a few await their turn), come in crisp blues and whites, with a wall of wood, Bose sound systems and excellent walk-in showers. As for the New Forest, walk, cycle or kayak though it. A great forest base.

Rooms	17 doubles, 9 twin/doubles: £95–£320.
	2 cottages for 4: £500–£1,400.
	Singles from £100.
Meals	Lunch from £5.
	Dinner: in the bar from £12;
	in the restaurant, 3 courses, £30–£35.
	Afternoon tea from £15.
	Sunday lunch £19.95–£23.95.
Closed	Never.

Paul Brown
The Master Builder's House Hotel
Bucklers Hard, Beaulieu,
Brockenhurst, SO42 7XB

Tel	+44 (0)1590 616253
Email	enquiries@themasterbuilders.co.uk
Web	www.themasterbuilders.co.uk

Castle House

Hereford's loveliest hotel stands 200 paces from the city's magnificent 11th-century cathedral, home to the Mappa Mundi. It's English to its core with a beautiful garden that overlooks what remains of the castle moat – in summer you can eat here watching ducks glide by. Inside, the lap of luxury: a fine staircase, painted panelling, a delicious restaurant for the best food in town. Big bedrooms are lavish. Those in the main house are more traditional (the top-floor suite runs all the way along the front of the house); those in the townhouse (a 30-second stroll) are distinctly 21st century. All have a smart country-house feel with beautiful fabrics, super-comfy beds, crisp white linen, excellent bathrooms with L'Occitane essential oils. Seriously good food, much from the owner's nearby farm, waits in the restaurant, perhaps beetroot panna cotta, roast bream with saffron mash, banana mousse with chocolate brownies. You can walk it off along the river Wye, which runs through the park behind. Hereford has lots to offer: pop-up opera, guided walks, Evensong in the cathedral, the Three Choirs Festival in July.

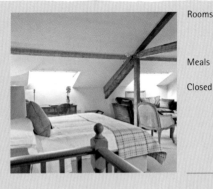

Rooms	4 doubles: £155-£200.
	16 suites for 2: £225-£260.
	4 singles: £140. Dinner, B&B from £100 per person.
Meals	Lunch from £5. Dinner, 3 courses, about £35. Sunday lunch from £18.50.
Closed	Never.

George Watkins
Castle House
Castle Street,
Hereford, HR1 2NW

Tel	+44 (0)1432 356321
Email	info@castlehse.co.uk
Web	www.castlehse.co.uk

The Verzon

This English auberge has a cute rustic style and serves some seriously good food. It sits on the Hereford to Ledbury road and is owned by William and Kate Chase, farmers who turn their potatoes and apples into Chase vodka and gin. Not that this is the limit of their world. They also rear cattle and pigs and have a vineyard in the Lubéron. The Verzon exists to bring it all together – a gin and tonic on the terrace in summer, then a lovely dinner washed down by French wines. Most of the food is sourced within 30 miles, perhaps a hoppy Hereford rarebit, a perfect Chase steak, an ambrosial pecan tart with espresso mousse. Interiors mix old and new playfully, with timber frames and Union-Jack sofas in the bar, then a white marble fireplace in the theatrical dining room. Bedrooms have warm colours, crisp linen and robes in fine bathrooms. Two have baths in the room, those at the back have views over fields to the Malvern Hills. Local ales and a roaring fire wait in the bar, while the Chase distillery is up the road, with tours easily arranged. Don't miss Hereford cathedral for the Mappa Mundi.

Rooms	4 twin/doubles: £90–£140. 3 suites for 2: £160–£180. 1 single: £80. Extra beds £15 p.p.
Meals	Lunch from £12. Dinner, 3 courses, £30–£40. Sunday lunch £22–£27. Afternoon tea from £15.
Closed	Never.

Will & Kate Chase
The Verzon
Hereford Road, Trumpet,
Ledbury, HR8 2PZ

Tel	+44 (0)1531 670381
Email	info@verzonhouse.com
Web	www.verzonhouse.com

Entry 92   Map 2

Brooks Country House

Led Zeppelin used to stay here when recording at studios on a nearby farm, and there's definitely a bit of a rock-star feel to the place. A big house in the country, a swimming pool in the kitchen garden and its own vineyard that produces wine for the restaurant… There's a rather good view, too, a clean sweep over ten miles of rolling country to rising mountains. The house once stood in 1,000 acres and now has a mere 12, but the land beyond is owned by the National Trust and you can walk straight out, skirt a copse and find yourself at a 14th-century church. As for the hotel – smart, but relaxed, with down-to-earth Andrew and Carla at the helm. Expect an open fire in the sitting room, wood floors in the restaurant, and cowhide rugs in a bar that opens onto a sun-trapping garden. Nicely priced rooms are scattered about, some grander, others smaller, all with good beds, warm colours and lovely bathrooms; and there's an apartment for four in the grounds if you want to look after yourselves. As for the food, it's earthy stuff; homemade soups, a local rib-eye, a sinful chocolate tart. Hard to beat. *Minimum stay: 2 nights at weekends. Pets by arrangement.*

Rooms	14 twin/doubles, 6 four-posters: £79-£169. 2 suites for 2: £99-£169. 3 trucks for 2: £99-£139. Singles £89-£119. Dinner, B&B £60-£80 per person. Extra bed/sofabed £10-£20 per person per night.
Meals	Dinner £18-£24 (not Sundays). Sunday lunch from £19-£23.
Closed	Never.

Carla & Andrew Brooks
Brooks Country House
Pengethley Park,
Ross-on-Wye, HR9 6LL
Tel +44 (0)1989 730211
Email info@brookscountryhouse.com
Web www.brookscountryhouse.com

The Bridge House

Kevin and Kathryn left high-flying jobs to cook, clean, polish and shine; they couldn't be happier. Their new home is this attractive 17th-century merchant's house with the best view in town. Lawns run down to the river Wye, then views shoot up the other side to St Mary's church. Inside, you find original elm floors and painted beamed ceilings, but the feel is contemporary, with cool colours, beautiful armchairs and antler chandeliers in the sitting room. Bedrooms have an easy elegance: comfy beds, crisp linen, pretty art, the odd timber frame. Five have the view, two have a claw-foot bath, others have power showers, a couple on high can be taken together. Breakfast is delicious, with doors in the sun room that fold back to drink in the view. Walk in the hills, kayak on the Wye, cycle in the Forest of Dean. Come home to an honesty bar in the sitting room and three terraces in the gorgeous garden, where colourful beds flourish. Wilton Castle, a 12th-century ruin, stands across the field; Hereford is close for the Mappa Mundi; good local restaurants wait. Dogs are welcome. *Minimum stay: 2 nights at weekends.*

Rooms	6 doubles, 2 twin/doubles: £95–£130. Singles £80.
Meals	Restaurants within walking distance.
Closed	16–27 December, 2 January – 1 February.

Kevin & Kathryn Whyte
The Bridge House
Wilton,
Ross-on-Wye, HR9 6AA
Tel   +44 (0)1989 562655
Email   info@bridgehouserossonwye.co.uk
Web   www.bridgehouserossonwye.co.uk

Entry 94   Map 2

Wilton Court Restaurant with Rooms

This Grade-II listed house dates to 1510 and looks across the lane to the river Wye: herons dive, otters swim, kingfishers nest. Roses ramble outside, happy guests potter within. This is a small hotel with pretty rooms, good food and owners that care. Bedrooms upstairs come in different shapes and sizes, but all have style. Those at the front have watery views, William Morris wallpaper, lots of space, perhaps a four-poster. A couple of rooms are small (as is their price), but, along with several others, have recently been refurbished. Expect lots of colour, a wall of paper, white bathrooms and sofas in the bigger rooms. Back downstairs there's a bar for pre-dinner drinks, a wood-burner in the panelled library, then a conservatory restaurant for tasty food, perhaps Shropshire blue cheese soufflé, Herefordshire beef with savoy cabbage, caramel panna cotta with vanilla ice cream. Berries from a Grade-I listed mulberry tree in the garden are turned into sorbets and pies. You can cross the lane to a second garden for drinks by the river in summer. Ross is a five-minute stroll. *Minimum stay: 2 nights at weekends.*

Rooms	4 doubles, 5 twin/doubles, 1 four-poster: £135–£185. 1 family room for 4: £165–£205. Singles from £100.
Meals	Lunch snacks from £6.95. Lunch, 2–3 courses, £16.95–£19.95. Dinner, set menu, 2–3 courses, £27.50–£32.50; à la carte, 3 courses, £35–£40.
Closed	2–19 January.

Roger & Helen Wynn
Wilton Court Restaurant with Rooms
Wilton Lane, Wilton,
Ross-on-Wye, HR9 6AQ
Tel   +44 (0)1989 562569
Email   info@wiltoncourthotel.com
Web   www.wiltoncourthotel.com

North House

Here's an Isle of Wight hotel beautifully remodelled in chic cosmopolitan style, while keeping lovely old fireplaces and other period features intact. Three listed buildings – an 1820s built theatre and two Georgian townhouses – are combined with an impressive frontage on a quiet road. A couple of minutes away downhill is Cowes High Street, with shops, restaurants and a hubbub of boatie endeavours, at its most lively during race weeks. Bedrooms come in three sizes, all immaculately furnished with well-chosen bed linens and metro-tiled bathrooms; from some you can watch the water traffic passing on the Solent. Larger rooms have free-standing baths, perfect after blowy coastal walks or days out at island attractions. There's no hotel parking, but staff will advise – they aim to please with personalised service. Downstairs, there are stylish spaces to relax – the traditional library is perfect for reading or catching up with some work, the bar and 'Oyster Store' restaurant are also open to the public. Outside, take a dip in the small heated pool all year round, with deckchairs and a neat suntrap terrace for summer.

Rooms	14 twin/doubles: £145–£245.
Meals	Continental and cooked breakfast included. Dinner, 3 courses, £20–£45. Pubs/restaurants 2-minute walk.
Closed	Never.

The Team at North House
North House
Sun Hill,
Cowes, PO31 7HY

Tel	+44 (0)1983 209453
Email	reservations@northhousecowes.co.uk
Web	www.northhousecowes.co.uk

Hillside

Is it an art gallery, a smallholding or a cool hotel? Whatever it is, Hillside is a great little place to wash up for a couple of nights. It stands at the foot of forested hills with views over Ventnor and out to sea. Outside, five acres of lawn, field and woodland are home to Hebridean sheep, free-range chickens, red squirrels and white doves; there are beehives, too, and a stunning kitchen garden that provides much for the table. Inside, you find a wonderland in white. There's a cute bar with a wood-burner, a sitting room with Danish leather sofas, an airy restaurant for the freshest food, then a conservatory that opens onto a terrace for afternoon tea in the sun. Inside, 286 pieces of art hang on the walls, but it's the food that counts most; the hotel has its own fishing boat and rears cattle in nearby fields. And it's delicious stuff, as fresh as can be, perhaps Ventnor Bay scallops with chorizo and Hillside honey, local rack of lamb with a red wine jus and garden greens, pear tarte tatin with edible wild flowers. Uncluttered bedrooms are a treat, those at the front have the view. *Minimum stay: 2 nights at weekends.*

Rooms	6 doubles, 2 twin/doubles, 1 twin: £156–£206. 3 singles: £78–£143. 2 apartments for 4: £206–£292. Dinner B&B from £108 p.p.
Meals	Lunch, 2 courses, £20. Dinner £24–£28.
Closed	Never.

Gert Bach
Hillside
151 Mitchell Avenue,
Ventnor, PO38 1DR

Tel	+44 (0)1983 852271
Email	mail@hillsideventnor.co.uk
Web	www.hillsideventnor.co.uk

The Milk House

The gardens at Sissinghurst Castle were designed by Vita Sackville-West. They're some of the loveliest in the land and if you stay at this charming village pub, you can stroll over after breakfast, through apple orchards and bluebell woods. As for the Milk House, it's a great base from which to explore – stylish, welcoming, nicely priced. It's also a place for excellent food, with seasonal produce mostly sourced within 20 miles. In summer, you decant onto a big terrace with an outside bar and a wood-fired pizza oven, not a bad spot for a crispy margherita and a glass of Pimm's. There's a duck pond, a lawned garden, views over open country, even a four-day festival in August (local bands, theatre, face painting, lots of food). Interiors have an easy style: woven willow lampshades, a sofa in front of the fire, a timber-framed dining room for fabulous food, perhaps twice-baked Stilton soufflé, grilled mackerel with roasted fennel, After Eight crème brûlée with brandy butter brioche. Beautiful bedrooms are crisply uncluttered. Expect chic fabrics, super beds, excellent bathrooms, a sofa if there's room.

Rooms	3 doubles, 1 twin: £120–£150. Extra bed/sofabed £10 p.p. per night.
Meals	Lunch from £6. Dinner, 3 courses, about £30. Sunday lunch from £15.
Closed	Rarely.

Dane & Sarah Allchorne
The Milk House
The Street, Sissinghurst,
Cranbrook, TN17 2JG
Tel   +44 (0)1580 720200
Email   fresh@themilkhouse.co.uk
Web   www.themilkhouse.co.uk

The Barrow House

You get a little time travel at the Barrow House: a 14th-century inn, 17th-century timber frames, 21st-century comfort and design. It's a great little place – friendly and stylish with super food and all sorts of libations waiting at the bar. It sits in a pretty village surrounded by open country with Leeds Castle up the road. Known as the George for centuries, it's name was changed in deference to the Bronze Age barrow that rises in a field on the edge of the village. Back at the inn, there's a smart terrace for lunch in the sun, and a couple of open fires inside to keep things cosy. They serve their own ale, craft beers and well-priced wines, but you can pop in for an espresso, too. Lovely rooms have big beds, pretty fabrics and smart TVs, perhaps timber frames or a wonky floor; bathrooms are a treat. As for the food, most is sourced within 20 miles. You'll find soups and sharing plates, burgers and fish and chips, or a three-course feast, perhaps smoked salmon, slow-cooked beef, marmalade Bakewell tart.

Rooms	2 doubles, 1 twin/double: £120-£160. Extra bed £10 p.p. per night.
Meals	Lunch, 2-3 courses, £12-15. Dinner, 3 courses, about £25.
Closed	Never.

Dane & Sarah Allchorne
The Barrow House
The Street,
Egerton, TN27 9DJ

Tel	+44 (0)1233 756599
Email	digin@thebarrowhouse.co.uk
Web	www.thebarrowhouse.co.uk

The Relish

It's not just the super-comfy interiors that make The Relish such a tempting port of call. There's a sense of generosity here: a drink on the house each night in the sitting room; tea and cakes on tap all day; free internet throughout. This is a grand 1850s merchant's house on the posh side of town — lovely old bricks and mortar, softly contemporary interiors. Laura and Rakesh took over recently and have already pulled out the paintbrushes, so wind up the cast-iron staircase to find bedrooms that make you smile. You get Hypnos beds with padded headboards, crisp white linen and pretty throws. There's a sense of space, a sofa if there's room, big mirrors and lovely bathrooms. All are great value for money. Downstairs candles flicker on the mantelpieces above an open fire, the high-ceilinged dining room comes with stripped floors and padded benches and in summer you can decamp onto the terrace for breakfast, a communal garden stretching out beyond. You're one street back from Folkestone's cliff-top front for big sea views. Steps lead down to smart gardens, the promenade and waterside restaurants.

Rooms	9 doubles: £98–£150.
	1 single: £70–£75. Singles £88–£140.
Meals	Restaurants nearby.
Closed	23–30 December.

Laura & Rakesh Sharma
The Relish
4 Augusta Gardens,
Folkestone, CT20 2RR

Tel	+44 (0)1303 850952
Email	reservations@hotelrelish.co.uk
Web	www.hotelrelish.co.uk

Read's Restaurant with Rooms

For the last 40 years David and Rona have been whisking up ambrosial food for the world and his wife to eat. On its own that's an incredible achievement, but to do so at the highest level is extraordinary. What's more, they make no fuss about it, just come to work every day and excel at what they do, a testament to their dedication and love of good food. As for Read's, it's a restaurant with rooms that happens to be a country house set in five acres of lawned gardens that include – no surprise – a productive kitchen garden. Inside, elegance at every turn. There's a sitting-room bar for pre-dinner drinks, then three dining rooms, where you eat at clothed tables, perhaps a Montgomery Cheddar soufflé, wild mallard with blackberries, Cox apple mousse with toffee apple jelly and cinnamon ice cream. Bedrooms are just as good, country-house splendour in spades. Expect decanters of sherry, Roberts radios, beds dressed in crisp white linen, smart bathrooms with white robes. Don't miss the orchards at Brogdale, where thousands of varieties of apples, pears, plums and cherries are on show.

Rooms	5 doubles, 1 twin/double: £165–£195. Singles from £125. Dinner, B&B from £135 p.p.
Meals	Lunch £28. Dinner £60.
Closed	Sunday & Monday. 1st 2 weeks in January, 1st 2 weeks in September. 25-27 December.

David & Rona Pitchford
Read's Restaurant with Rooms
Macknade Manor, Canterbury Road,
Faversham, ME13 8XE

Tel	+44 (0)1795 535344
Email	enquiries@reads.com
Web	www.reads.com

Albion House

This is quite some house, a Regency pile that dates to 1790, with huge rooms, high ceilings and grandeur at every turn. It stands at the top of a hill in the middle of town with fine views over the Royal Harbour. Incredibly, it was left to decay by its last inhabitants, Ramsgate Town Council, whose headquarters this was until 2008. Now, after a long renovation, interiors shine, mixing contemporary design with the feel of a colonial gentleman's club. There's a fire in reception, watery views through big windows in the restaurant, then a fabulous bar with a grand piano, exotic pot plants, a roaring fire, and sofas everywhere. Classical prints are jammed on the wall, the bar itself came from the town hall. The whole place is a work of art, nothing is here by accident. Enjoy the treatment room, steam room and the vaulted cavern for wine tastings. Big bedrooms get smaller as you climb the house, but the best views are at the top. Expect good beds, crisp linen, neutral colours, robes in white marble bathrooms. Beaches, gardens and cliff-top walks wait, but don't miss afternoon tea.
Minimum stay: 2 nights at weekends April-September. Pets by arrangement.

Rooms	13 twin/doubles: £89–£245. 1 suite for 2: £180–£345. Dinner, B&B from £80 p.p.
Meals	Lunch from £5. Dinner, 2-3 courses, £20–£35. Sunday lunch from £16. Afternoon tea £16.
Closed	Never.

Ben & Emma Irvine
Albion House
Albion Place,
Ramsgate, CT11 8HQ

Tel	+44 (0)1843 606630
Email	enquiries@albionhouseramsgate.co.uk
Web	www.albionhouseramsgate.co.uk

Sands Hotel Margate

Hoteliers don't do things by halves, and Nick is a case in point. He bought a crumbling pile, knocked the place down, then built it back up again. The result is a delicious hotel with huge views of beach and sea, a view framed triumphantly by walls of glass in the enormous restaurant and bar. Coastal light floods the room, there's a balcony for afternoon tea, three chandeliers hanging above the bar, crushed velvet banquettes to salute Victorian roots and, with Turner Contemporary a five-minute stroll along the seafront, big canvases that resemble the great man's work. Bedrooms have bags of style; nine have sea views, six have balconies and all have chic fabrics, padded bedheads, smart TVs and robes in fine bathrooms. There's a roof terrace above for the best views in town and an ice-cream parlour and pizzeria below, but you'll want to stop in the middle for the food as well as the view; perhaps gin and juniper-cured salmon, or confit pork belly with candied apple, finished off with a spiced pineapple tarte tatin. Canterbury, Broadstairs and Ramsgate are close and the train from Victoria takes less than two hours. *Minimum stay: 2 nights at weekends in high season.*

Rooms	10 doubles, 10 twin/doubles: £120–£210. Dinner, B&B £95–£130 p.p. Extra bed/sofabed available £20–£40 p.p.p.n.
Meals	Lunch from £11.50. Dinner, 3 courses, £35. Cream tea £6.50. Afternoon tea £14.95.
Closed	Never.

Nick Conington
Sands Hotel Margate
16 Marine Drive,
Margate, CT9 1DH

Tel	+44 (0)1843 228228
Email	info@sandshotelmargate.co.uk
Web	www.sandshotelmargate.co.uk

The Cartford Inn

This quirky inn is full of its own delights, not least its stylish interiors, fabulous food and helpful staff. This might explain why it was named Best Inn in Britain in 2016, a richly deserved award. Julie and Patrick love their world and can't stop spending money on it. Recently they opened a gorgeous deli on the terrace and built two gob-smacking suites on stilts overlooking the river. It's a mecca for locals, who come to eat, drink and gossip. Outside, views stretch across to the Trough of Bowland. Inside, delicious food waits, perhaps fresh crab gnocchi, roasted Lytham poussin, Ovaltine panna cotta with dark chocolate mousse. The bar, with its cool art and roaring fire, is a great place to linger over a pint of local ale, but a courtyard garden will draw you out in good weather. Bedrooms have style in spades: gilded sleigh beds, signature wallpapers, river views, perhaps a roll-top bath in the room; the penthouse has a rooftop terrace, too. You can follow the river on a two-mile circular walk. Don't miss Blackpool, a proper northern town. Brilliant.

Rooms	11 doubles: £130–£230. 2 suites for 2: £230–£250. 2 family rooms for 3-4: £150. Singles £80–£150.
Meals	Lunch from £8.50; not Monday. Dinner, 3 courses, £25–£35.
Closed	25–26 December.

Patrick & Julie Beaume
The Cartford Inn
Cartford Lane, Little Eccleston,
Preston, PR3 0YP

Tel	+44 (0)1995 670166
Email	info@thecartfordinn.co.uk
Web	www.thecartfordinn.co.uk

The Inn at Whitewell

It is almost impossible to imagine a day when a better inn will grace the English landscape. Everything here is perfect. The inn sits just above the river Hodder, and doors in the bar lead onto a terrace where guests can enjoy five-mile views across parkland to rising fells. Inside, fires roar, newspapers wait, there are beams, sofas, maps and copies of *Wisden*. Bedrooms, some in the Coach House, are exemplary and come with real luxury, perhaps a peat fire, a lavish four-poster, a fabulous Victorian power shower. All have beautiful fabrics, top linen and gadgets galore; many have the marvellous view – you can fall asleep at night to the sound of the river. There are bar meals for those who want to watch their weight (the Whitewell fish pie is rightly famous) or a restaurant for splendid food, so dig into seared scallops, Bowland lamb, a plate of local cheese (the Queen once popped in for lunch). Elsewhere, a wine shop in reception, seven miles of private fishing and countryside as good as any in the land. Dogs and children are very welcome. Magnificent.

Rooms	17 doubles, 5 twin/doubles: £137-£270. 1 suite for 2: £235-£270. Singles £99-£218.
Meals	Bar meals from £8. Dinner £25-£35.
Closed	Never.

Charles Bowman
The Inn at Whitewell
Dunsop Road, Whitewell,
Clitheroe, BB7 3AT

Tel	+44 (0)1200 448222
Email	reception@innatwhitewell.com
Web	www.innatwhitewell.com

Abbots Oak Manor

Sarah and Anthony have brought this listed house back from the brink with style and a real passion for the place. The old bones: dark beams, stone mullion windows and ornate carvings, flatter the contemporary luxury of the interiors. The sophisticated bedrooms have a calm, light-grey colour scheme, excellent mattresses on king-size beds, one has a working fireplace, the suite can fit an extra two guests, all have Nespresso machines. The en-suite bathrooms are fabulous: double-ended tap-free baths with music at the touch of a button, and great showers. Enjoy dinner in the chandeliered dining room, perhaps rump and belly of lamb with wilted baby gem lettuce followed by jasmine mousse with cherry soup and lavender biscuits. Seriously good food — as seasonal, foraged and local as possible — is served at breakfast too, with linen and vintage china, at one table in the 'small' dining room. There's a smörgåsbord of craft gins to sample at the bar and the grounds are being beautifully restored. Marvellous. *Parking on-site.*

Rooms	7 doubles: £145–£225.
	1 suite for 2: £225.
	Extra beds £50 incl. breakfast.
Meals	Dinner £30.
	Children's dinner £15.
	Pubs/restaurants 2 miles.
Closed	Rarely.

Sarah Kurr
Abbots Oak Manor
Warren Hills Road,
Abbots Oak, Coalville, LE67 4UY

Tel	+44 (0)1530 833952
Email	sarahvale1@hotmail.com
Web	www.abbotsoak.co.uk

Washingborough Hall

In its day Lincoln was one of the most important cities in England. Its castle holds one of the four original copies of the Magna Carta and was built by William the Conqueror in 1068; its cathedral dates to 1090 and remains one of the finest in Europe. All of which makes it a great city to visit, and if you want to beat a peaceful retreat into the country at the end of the day, this is the place to stay. It sits two miles east of town in a small village on the river Witham — footpaths by the water lead back into town. As for this Georgian rectory, you'll find smart lawns to the front, then a big welcome within — Edward and Lucy go out of their way to make your stay special. There's a wood-burner in the hall, a breakfast room with garden views, a sitting-room bar for afternoon tea, then a light-filled orangery restaurant. Stylish bedrooms offer unstinting comforts. Rooms at the front are bigger and have the view, all have good beds, bold wallpapers, excellent bathrooms, a sofa if there's room. As for the food, there's posh fish and chips in the bar or sea bass with spring greens in the orangery.

Rooms	12 doubles, 3 twin/doubles, 2 four-posters: £85–£175. 1 suite for 2: £175–£195. 2 singles: £65–£85.
Meals	Lunch from £5.50. Dinner, 3 courses, £25–£35. Sunday lunch from £18.50.
Closed	Never.

Lucy & Edward Herring
Washingborough Hall
Church Hill,
Washingborough, LN4 1BE
Tel	+44 (0)1522 790340
Email	enquiries@washingboroughhall.com
Web	www.washingboroughhall.com

The William Cecil

This attractive townhouse hotel stands yards from the gates of the Burghley estate. Inside, interiors offer a pleasing mix of English quirkiness and splendour. Downstairs, informality reigns. There are armchairs in front of the fire in the bar, smart wicker tables in the conservatory, doors onto a lovely terrace in summer, then hanging lamps and half-panelling in the colourful restaurant. The food is fresh and local with seasonal delights that include game from the estate. You might find lobster mousse with avocado ice-cream, slow-cooked Burghley venison casserole, lemon curd pie with lime sorbet. You can walk it all off with a stroll through historic Stamford or spin over to Burghley for one of the finest Elizabethan houses in the realm. Come back to country-house bedrooms that mix eclectic Rajasthan furniture with a little English decorum. You'll find beautiful art, a wall of paper, perhaps a day bed or a ceiling rose. Some have views onto the estate, all have good bathrooms, the best with roll top tubs and vast walk-in showers. Dogs don't fare badly either with Union Jack beds.

Rooms	20 doubles, 7 twin/doubles: £100–£180.
Meals	Lunch from £6.50. Dinner from £12. Sunday lunch, 3 courses, £24.50.
Closed	Never.

Paul Brown
The William Cecil
St Martins,
Stamford, PE9 2LJ

Tel   +44 (0)1780 750070
Email   enquiries@thewilliamcecil.co.uk
Web   www.thewilliamcecil.co.uk

The Princess Victoria

Make yourself at home – it'll take five seconds – and while away an afternoon in one of the few remaining gin palaces in London. Beneath soaring ceilings, a fabulous collection of 120 gins takes centre stage, cossetted by staff who really know what they're talking about. The place buzzes, thanks to craft beers, seasonal ciders and a modern pub menu based on great ingredients. The beef is aged in-house and the pizzas are stone-baked. Eat in the bar, or in the grand dining room, where bare-knuckle boxing once took place. Off here is a secret courtyard garden, a suntrap for cocktails. Given the location, the bedrooms are unexpectedly quiet havens. Enjoy rainhead showers, Nespresso machines and seamless air con. Later, after a great (weekends only) brunch, take a bus to leafy Holland Park, or Portobello Market and Notting Hill. Your closest hub is Shepherd's Bush, a 20-minute walk.

Rooms	1 twin/double £99–£129. 4 doubles: £99–£129.
Meals	Lunch from £9. Dinner from £11. Sunday lunch from £13.
Closed	25–26 December.

Reservations Team
The Princess Victoria
217 Uxbridge Road,
Shepherd's Bush, London, W12 9DH
Tel   +44 (0)20 8749 4466
Email   info@princessvictoria.co.uk
Web   www.princessvictoria.co.uk

Temple Lodge Club

Temple Lodge, once home to the painter Sir Frank Brangwyn, is sandwiched between a courtyard and a lushly landscaped garden. The peace is remarkable making it a very restful place – simple yet human and warmly comfortable, a nourishing experience. Michael and his devoted team run it with quiet energy. You breakfast overlooking the garden, there are newspapers to browse, a library instead of TVs. Bedrooms are surprisingly stylish: pretty art, crisp linen, no clutter, a hint of country chic. They're exceptional value for money, too, so book well in advance. Some rooms have garden views, only a couple have their own bathrooms and loo; if you don't mind that, you'll be happy. The Thames passes by at the end of the road, the Riverside Studios is round the corner for theatre and film, and the Gate Vegetarian Restaurant is across the courtyard, a well-known eatery, its food so good even committed carnivores can't resist. It was also Brangwyn's studio, hence the artist's window. The house is a non-denominational Christian centre with two services a week, which you may take or leave as you choose.

Rooms	1 double; 2 doubles with separate bath/shower: £108-£121. 1 double sharing bathroom: £77-£93. 5 singles, either with separate bathroom or sharing: £59-£73. Extra bed/sofabed £12-£14 p.p. per night.
Meals	Continental breakfast included. Vegetarian restaurant across courtyard.
Closed	Never.

Alicja Fediow & Peter Van Breda
Temple Lodge Club
51 Queen Caroline Street,
Hammersmith, London, W6 9QL
Tel   +44 (0)20 8748 8388
Email   booking@templelodgeclub.com
Web   www.templelodgeclub.com

Artist Residence London

In the future, if a book is written about London hotels, they will divide it into two periods – before and after Artist Residence London. Because this gorgeous small hotel is a game changer, a new template of British cool, a space designed wholly to exercise your pleasure receptors. It proves resoundingly that small is more beautiful than big ever can be and while large hotels will try to copy it, they'll fail miserably, unable to match its intimacy, or the fantastic staff who look after you all the way. So what do you get? A small slice of heaven between Pimlico and the King's Road. It's a phoenix from the ashes, a Thomas Cubitt pub recently rescued from neglect. The cellar bar, with pop art and exposed brick walls, must qualify as one of London's coolest; the sitting room has fat sofas in front of a roaring fire; the Cambridge Street Café offers lovely food in a stylish, relaxed setting. Bedrooms are flawless: cool art, chic fabrics, the best beds, power-showered bathrooms. Smaller rooms are divine, bigger rooms have sofas, the suites have free-standing baths. Battersea Park is close.

Rooms	8 doubles: £170–£280.
	2 suites for 2: £290–£425.
	Singles £150–£250.
Meals	Lunch from £9.50.
	Dinner, 3 courses, about £35.
Closed	Never.

Charlie & Justin Salisbury
Artist Residence London
52 Cambridge St, Pimlico, SW1V 4QQ

Tel	+44 (0)20 3019 8610
Email	london@artistresidence.co.uk
Web	www.artistresidence.co.uk/our-hotels/london/

Lime Tree Hotel

You'll be hard pressed to find better value in the centre of town. The Lime Tree — two elegant Georgian townhouses — stands less than a mile from Buckingham Palace, with Westminster, Sloane Square and Piccadilly all a short stroll. Add warm interiors, kind owners and a smart gastropub waiting round the corner and you've unearthed a London gem. The airy dining room serves a mean breakfast and is soon to turn into a café, with light meals served throughout the day. Rooms are just the ticket: smart without being lavish, all with mod cons. Expect warm colours, crisp linen, attractive wallpaper and excellent bathrooms (most have big showers). One on the ground floor has doors onto the garden; others on first floor have high ceilings; those at the top (a few stairs!) are cosy in the eaves; rooms at the back are the quietest. Charlotte and Matt are hands-on and will point you in the right direction, while there's a tiny sitting room for guide books and a computer for guests to use. The Thomas Cubitt pub — 50 paces from the front door — serves great food. A very handy base for the Chelsea Flower Show. *Minimum stay: 2 nights at weekends.*

Rooms	12 doubles, 4 twins: £155–£230.
	6 singles: £105–£180.
	3 triples: £200–£260.
Meals	Restaurants nearby.
Closed	Never.

Charlotte & Matt Goodsall
Lime Tree Hotel
135 Ebury Street,
Belgravia, London, SW1W 9QU
Tel   +44 (0)20 7730 8191
Email   info@limetreehotel.co.uk
Web   www.limetreehotel.co.uk

11 Cadogan Gardens

You're cared for here by super-friendly staff; it's smart but not stuffy and the location is great. A short walk takes you to gawp at the world's most expensive brands – Chanel, Tiffany's, Prada and Hermes – and even if you can't afford to buy anything you can always *faire du leche-vitrines* as the French say. Walk to view the pretty pastel-hued houses of Chelsea, visit the swinging King's Road, explore the Chelsea Physic Garden or the Saatchi Gallery. The brilliant Victoria and Albert museum is just over half a mile away as is the Natural History museum. Afternoon tea is a fancy affair but you can move swiftly on to chocolate cocktails inspired by Sir Hans Sloane, one of the first importers of cocoa from Jamaica. If you prefer to eat in, then the Hans Bar and Grill serves fresh modern British food conjured up by chef Adam England.

Rooms	25 doubles: £280–£350. 25 suites: £430–£4000. Extra beds available. 6 singles: £250.
Meals	Lunch from £15. Dinner, 3 courses, from £45. Afternoon tea from £25.
Closed	Never.

Reservations Team
11 Cadogan Gardens
Chelsea,
London, SW3 2RJ

Tel	+44 (0)20 7730 7000
Email	reservations@11cadogangardens.com
Web	www.11cadogangardens.com

The Levin Hotel

This is shopaholic heaven – Harrods at one end of the street, Harvey Nicks at the other. As for the Levin, it sits quietly on Basil Street, a peaceful retreat in the middle of Knightsbridge. A lively café/bar/restaurant acts as the hub; you can enjoy breakfast here of freshly backed croissants, nip back early for afternoon tea or a filling lunch; perhaps Cornish mussels in cider cream and parsley to start then a tasty spinach, blue cheese & red onion frittata as your main. If that's not enough, nip next door to the Capital (their sister hotel) where you'll find Outlaw's, a Michelin star restaurant. Bedrooms are spread over four floors with a lift to carry you up, though you may prefer to walk; a contemporary chandelier with an 18-metre drop fills the stairwell. As for the rooms, some are bigger, others smaller, but all have the same crisp style: bold colours, hand-stitched beds, marble bathrooms, books galore. Bigger rooms have sofas, all have white robes, crisp linen, Bose radios and flat-screen TVs. You get air conditioning and a handy smartphone, too. There's a full concierge service, iPads are available at reception. Hyde Park is close. *Pets by arrangement.*

Rooms	3 doubles, 8 twin/doubles: £245–£479.
	1 suite for 2: £395–£619.
	Extra bed/sofabed £45 p.p. per night.
Meals	Lunch from £5.50. Dinner, 3 courses,
	about £30. Afternoon tea from £22.99.
Closed	Never.

Kate Levin
The Levin Hotel
28 Basil Street, Knightsbridge,
London, SW3 1AS

Tel	+44 (0)20 7589 6286
Email	reservations@thelevinhotel.co.uk
Web	www.thelevinhotel.co.uk

The Grafton

Smart décor and a buzzy vibe make this West End pub with rooms a great place for couples planning a city break. Sit out on the secret roof terrace with a cocktail or a guest ale, sample the pan-Asian menu, stay in one of the smart bedrooms upstairs. Central London is waiting to be delved into: Oxford Street, Bond Street and Selfridges are a 15-minute walk, Soho and theatres are about the same distance and teeming with great places to eat – try the French House on Dean Street. Once you've shopped and eaten take a walk through Regent's Park and head back to your peaceful bedroom. Choose something to watch on Netflix, order a continental breakfast and free newspaper to be delivered in the morning.

Rooms	11 doubles: £145–£205.
Meals	Continental breakfast £12.
	Light bites from £4.50. Lunch & dinner from £8.50.
Closed	Never.

Reservations Team
The Grafton
72 Grafton Way, Fitzrovia,
London, W1T 5DU

Tel	+44 (0)20 7405 1521
Email	info@graftonarms.co.uk
Web	www.pubsandrooms.com

The Clerk & Well Pub & Rooms

On Clerkenwell Road, opposite Leather Lane Market, this old city pub has smart rooms above. Mingle with locals at the bar while you sample an ale or a cocktail then choose from the pan-Asian menu before heading out. Over the road the market throngs with office workers and tourists grabbing lunch – it's a street food paradise – try some falafel or a vegan burrito. Wander through the Hatton Garden jewellery quarter; St Paul's Cathedral and the British Museum are a 15-minute walk or you can be at the tube station in minutes. Back at base you can let yourself through the side door and up to your bedroom; all have Nespresso machines, mini fridges and TV, some have baths. Rooms at the front have thick fabric blinds and double glazing to shut out noise, while those at the back are completely quiet.

Rooms	8 doubles: £145–£205.
Meals	Continental breakfast £12. Light bites from £4.50. Lunch & dinner from £8.50
Closed	Never.

Reservations Team
The Clerk & Well Pub & Rooms
156 Clerkenwell Road,
London, EC1R 5DU

Tel	+44 (0)20 7837 8548
Email	info@theclerkandwell.co
Web	www.pubsandrooms.com

The One Tun Pub & Rooms

This stylish inn dates to 1759, but its moment of fame came in 1838, when Charles Dickens changed its name to the Three Cripples and made it Bill Sikes' watering hole of choice in *Oliver Twist*. These days it's a thriving local with a restaurant serving pan-Asian food and some beautiful bedrooms above the shop. It sits on peaceful Saffron Hill (home to Fagin and the Artful Dodger), with flower baskets and Victorian lanterns on the outside, then painted panelling and Chesterfield sofas within. You'll find English ales, fancy cocktails, wines from around the world, then some very popular Asian cooking, perhaps chilli salt squid, Asian pork belly with choy sum, vanilla ice cream topped with tamarind caramel. Bedrooms upstairs are delightful – crisp linen, beautiful fabrics, stylish wallpapers, robes in excellent bathrooms. Most are big, none are small, one has a decked terrace, all have comfy beds, coffee machines, smart TVs and super-fast WiFi. Breakfast (7.30am-11am) is brought to your room with a complimentary newspaper. St Paul's, the Barbican and the Tate Modern all within easy reach.

Rooms	8 doubles: £140–£215. Extra bed £25.
Meals	Continental breakfast £12. Lunch from £4.50. Dinner, 3 courses, about £30. Pub closed on Sundays.
Closed	Rarely.

Reservations Team
The One Tun Pub & Rooms
125 Saffron Hill,
London, EC1N 8QS

Tel	+44 (0)20 7405 1521
Email	info@onetun.co.uk
Web	www.pubsandrooms.com

The Tommyfield

The Tommyfield is a cool little find – a lively pub for a good pint, a restaurant serving tasty food, a small hotel with well-priced rooms that deliver in spades. It sits between Vauxhall and Kennington, with two tube lines to whizz you into town and three buses passing outside. Inside, you find wooden floors, high ceilings and the odd ionic pillar. Lamps hang above the bar, where you can order a pint of Wandle, then dig into posh fish and chips. Leather banquettes run along big windows, an open kitchen is on display, a couple of booths are nicely private. Rooms are the big surprise, some with painted panelling, others with planked walls. You get pop art, good beds, coffee machines and flat-screen TVs. Excellent bathrooms have walk-in power showers, two have claw-foot baths. On weekdays a continental breakfast is left in your fridge, on weekends the full English is on tap below. As for the food – half-price for residents – pies, steaks and burgers sit alongside pumpkin ravioli, Chateaubriand and banoffee pie. Tuesday is quiz night, Oval is close for the cricket.

Rooms	4 doubles, 2 twin/doubles: £109-£159. Cots available.
Meals	Continental breakfast included; cooked breakfast on weekends £6-£9. Lunch & dinner from £12.50. Sunday lunch from £13.50. Food half-price for residents.
Closed	Never.

Reservations Team
The Tommyfield
185 Kennington Lane, Kennington,
London, SE11 4EZ

Tel	+44 (0)20 7735 1061
Email	info@thetommyfield.co.uk
Web	www.pubsandrooms.com

The Victoria Inn

A great little pub in a trendy enclave with lovely staff, tasty food and chic rooms that don't cost a fortune. Outside, there's a shaded terrace for sunny days where you can watch local life pass by. Inside, you get a 21st-century makeover of a beautiful Victorian pub: original wood floors and windows, then colourful booths and banquettes. Craft beers and local ales wait at a fine old bar; spin round to the restaurant and find quirky local photos on exposed brick walls. Pull up a chair at one of the smart tables and dig into super food, perhaps pea and loveage soup, shepherds pie with buttered greens, chocolate fondant with blackberry sorbet. Bedrooms are a steal – 12 cost £110 or less. They're lovely, too: airy colours, local art, comfy beds, super bathrooms. You get coffee machines, flat-screen TVs and Bose WiFi speakers. Why spend a fortune in central London, when you can hang out with locals in a cool part of town? Sundays are fun – delicious roasts, live jazz in the evening. Peckham Rye station is a three-minute walk. There's a funky market, a lovely common and free parking, too.

Rooms	11 doubles, 3 twin/doubles: £90–£165. 1 family room for 4: £125–£165.
Meals	Lunch from £5. Dinner, 3 courses, £25–£30. Sunday lunch from £16.
Closed	Never.

Matt Hedges
The Victoria Inn
77 Choumert Road, Peckham,
London, SE15 4AR

Tel	+44 (0)20 7639 5052
Email	reservations@victoriainnpeckham.com
Web	www.victoriainnpeckham.com

Tulse Hill Hotel

This is a fantastic find, a beautiful hotel close to Herne Hill and its lovely park, Brixton and its hipster groove and Dulwich and its famous art gallery. There's been a hostelry on this spot for over 500 years. The current version is a dream, a delightful mix of old and new. A smart Georgian exterior gives way to beautiful interiors. You'll find open fires, panelled walls, then an airy restaurant with a wall of glass that opens onto a terrace for great food and a good pint. It draws a local crowd – who doesn't love having an excellent pub on their doorstep? Cool tunes float in the air, lights go down at night and candles flicker. Bedrooms upstairs are hard to fault: padded headboards, colourful throws, quirky art, robes in sparkling bathrooms. All have coffee machines, air-conditioning and flat-screen TVs. Spin down for a delicious dinner, perhaps salt cod fritters, a bavette steak, coconut panna cotta with pineapple and rum. Staff are lovely, don't miss Brockwell Park and its wonderful lido, perfect for summer days. Finally, the most coveted possession in London: a car park for guests!

Rooms	6 doubles: £115–£150. 2 family rooms for 4: £150–£165. 1 single: £85–£95.
Meals	Lunch from £7.50. Dinner, 3 courses, about £30. Sunday lunch from £16.
Closed	Never.

Avi Cohen
Tulse Hill Hotel
150 Norwood Road, Tulse Hill,
London, SE24 9AY

Tel	+44 (0)20 8671 7499
Email	sleep@tulsehillhotel.com
Web	www.tulsehillhotel.com

Entry 120   Map 3

Strattons

You arrive to find an exquisite Queen Anne villa that wouldn't look out of place in France, then you step inside and discover a contemporary art gallery with rooms. Strattons is a treasure trove of beautiful things. It is in constant flux, too – the new café/deli overflows with delicious treats and comes with a roof terrace, not a bad spot for afternoon tea. Back inside, you find august busts, contemporary chandeliers, stylish sofas to take the strain. Bedrooms are equally creative: a carved four-poster in priestly red, Botticelli's angels hovering on a wall, bedside lights that hang from the ceiling. Some have double-ended baths in the room, others a roof terrace with sun loungers. You breakfast in the deli on irresistible delights: natural yoghurt and muesli, sweet-smelling bacon rolls, the full cooked works. After which head off to the Brecks for walks through its magical forest or spin up to King's Lynn to explore its Hanseatic architecture. A very good dinner awaits your return, perhaps smoked haddock soufflé, spiced quail with poached pear, chocolate brownie with banana ice cream. *Minimum stay: 2 nights at weekends. Pets by arrangement.*

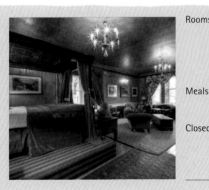

Rooms	6 doubles, 1 twin/double: £99–£244.
	5 suites for 2: £131–£254.
	2 apartments for 2: £154–£244.
	Singles £94–£234.
	Dinner, B&B £155–£310 per person.
	Extra bed £10–£45 per person per night.
Meals	Lunch from £6.
	Dinner, 3 courses, £30–£35. Sunday
	lunch from £14. Afternoon tea £15.50.
Closed	1 week over Christmas.

	Vanessa & Les Scott
	Strattons
	4 Ash Close,
	Swaffham, PE37 7NH
Tel	+44 (0)1760 723845
Email	enquiries@strattonshotel.com
Web	www.strattonshotel.com

Chalk & Cheese

Andrew and Bridget's Victorian schoolhouse stands on the village green. If its exterior gives the impression of English decorum, its interiors do the very opposite; the bust of Aristotle draped in a feather boa is a bit of a giveaway. It's all refreshingly original – interior design laced with humour. The big room takes centre stage, its high ceiling and stained glass giving an ecclesiastic feel. You'll find Cambodian lampshades and Vietnamese water puppets, mismatching sofas and a crackling fire, William Morris wallpaper and books by the hundred, then a quirky bar with light descending from on high. Homely bedrooms are warm, simple and nicely priced. One has a four-poster, another a slipper bath, two next door in a cute cottage can be taken together to self-cater. There's even a bunk house and a wheelchair-friendly bolthole in the garden. Pizzas fly from a wood-fired oven, while pea and ham soup, homemade cottage pie and sticky toffee pudding costs under £20. There's a conservatory breakfast room, a terrace for summer and a farm shop selling the odd antique. Good walks and the coast wait.

Rooms	3 doubles, 1 twin, 1 four-poster: £75–£95. 1 cottage for 2: £105–£125. 1 bunk room for 4: £35 per person. Singles from £65. Extra beds from £10. Self-catering option.
Meals	Lunch from £4.50. Dinner, 3 courses, £20–£25 (not Sun-Wed). Sunday lunch from £9.95.
Closed	Never.

Andrew & Bridget Archibald
Chalk & Cheese
1 Eastgate Street, Shouldham,
King's Lynn, PE33 0DD
Tel   +44 (0)1366 348039
Email   info@chalkandcheesenorfolk.co.uk
Web   www.bed-and-breakfast-west-norfolk.co.uk

Congham Hall

This is a beautiful Georgian merchant's house set in 30 acres of parkland. It's also a cool little spa hotel with an indoor pool and treatment rooms, a perfect blend of old and new. Outside, three gardeners grow flowers for the house, vegetables for the kitchen and keep the gardens looking serene. Inside, country house interiors have an elegant contemporary feel. There's an open fire in the sitting room, a chic bar with low-hanging lampshades, then an airy dining room for excellent local food, perhaps crayfish salad, slow-cooked chicken, hot chocolate fondant with banana ice cream. After which you'll need to atone, so roast away in the sauna before a dip in the pool; there are sunbeds and a hot tub on the decked terrace, too. Refurbished rooms are gorgeous. House rooms have beautiful fabrics and excellent beds. The suite has a balcony for breakfast, all have robes in striking bathrooms (one is entered through cupboard doors). Courtyard rooms are big and airy and open onto the kitchen garden. Children are welcome and have their own menu. Sandringham is close. There's tennis and croquet, too. *Minimum stay: 2 nights at weekends.*

Rooms	25 twin/doubles: £135-£260. 1 suite for 2: £275. Dinner, B&B from £110 p.p. Extra beds for children under 12 free.
Meals	Breakfast £8-£15. Lunch from £5. Dinner, 3 courses, about £35. Afternoon tea from £8.75. Sunday lunch, 3 courses, £27.50.
Closed	Rarely.

Julie Woodhouse
Congham Hall
Grimston,
King's Lynn, PE32 1AH
Tel   +44 (0)1485 600250
Email   info@conghamhallhotel.co.uk
Web   www.conghamhallhotel.co.uk

The White Horse

A smart little inn on the North Norfolk coast with beautiful views that shoot across tidal marshes to Scolt Head Island. At high tide boats bob, birds swoop and the water laps at the garden edge; at low tide, the marshes appear and fishermen come to harvest the mussels and oysters. In summer you can eat on the terrace and drink it all in, then drop down to the coastal path at the bottom of the garden and follow your nose. But the view here is weatherproofed – a big conservatory restaurant looks out on it all. It's a popular haunt for locals and visitors alike, who come for consistently good food, perhaps oysters from the bay, sea bass with squid risotto, lemon tart with a chocolate macaroon. There's a sunken garden that catches the sun, then an open fire in the locals' bar, where you'll find well-kept ales, the daily papers, bar billiards and sofas for a game of scrabble. Chic, uncluttered bedrooms have seaside colours, robes for spotless bathrooms, good beds and fine linen. Some in the main house have the view, dog-friendly garden rooms have terraces. Sandringham is close. *Minimum stay: 2 nights at weekends.*

Rooms	11 doubles, 4 twins: £100-£230.
	Extra beds £30 p.p. Cots £5. Dogs £10.
Meals	Lunch & bar meals from £8.95.
	Dinner from £13.95.
Closed	Never.

Cliff Nye & Family
The White Horse
Brancaster Staithe, PE31 8BY

Tel	+44 (0)1485 210262
Email	reception@whitehorsebrancaster.co.uk
Web	www.whitehorsebrancaster.co.uk

The Hoste

This iconic hotel sits a couple of miles back from Norfolk's sparkling north coast. It dates to the early 1600s and had one rather famous local – Nelson used the beautiful timbered bar as a recruiting post and would catch the stage to London from the front door after a good night's sleep. These days it's a social hub on the village green that pulses with life all year round, a great base from which to explore this stretch of heaven. Inside, beautiful bedrooms, delicious food, fine wines and quenching local ales all wait. You can eat in the panelled dining room, the historic bar, the buzzing conservatory or the airy garden room that opens onto a terrace, and the food is delicious, perhaps lobster risotto with Cromer crab, Norfolk venison with red cabbage, warm chocolate fondant with vanilla ice cream. There's a peaceful walled garden, a small spa for treatments, a cute little cinema that shows three films a day. Bedrooms are scattered about: contemporary delights at the Hoste; boutique elegance at Vine House; smart rooms and a vintage train carriage at Railway House; chic cottages for longer stays. A treat.

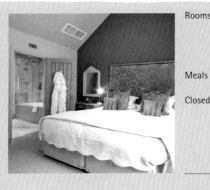

Rooms	62 twin/doubles: £140–£275.
	3 cottages for 6: £290.
	1 train carriage for 2: £195–£230.
	Singles from £120.
	Dinner, B&B from £95p.p.
Meals	Lunch from £6. Dinner, 3 courses, from £25. Sunday lunch from £14.
Closed	Never.

Martin De Sousa
The Hoste
The Green, Burnham Market,
King's Lynn, PE31 8HD

Tel   +44 (0)1328 738777
Email   reservations@thehoste.com
Web   www.thehoste.com

The Globe Inn at Wells-next-the-Sea

It's as English as England can be – a beautiful inn on a Georgian green, where Nelson used to catch the coach to London. Potter down to the water and find a sandy beach for family fun, then a small harbour, where day boats land their catch on the quay. As for the Globe, it's an inn for all seasons. Outside, there's a sun-trapping terrace at the front, a flower-filled courtyard where you can eat in summer, then a colourful roof terrace for guests. Inside, wood-burners sit at both ends of the bar, there are sofas and armchairs, games for rainy days, then local ales and excellent wines with which to wash down delicious local food. You eat in an airy restaurant with local art of the walls, perhaps clam linguini with chilli and garlic, dressed Wells crab or a rib-eye steak, then chocolate mousse with pistachio ice cream. Rooms above have the comfiest beds in the land. Those at the front have views of the green, all have crisp linen, padded heads and vintage tiles in sparkling bathrooms. Rooms connect for families, dogs are very welcome, boat trips can be arranged. Sandringham is up the road. *Minimum stay: 2 nights at weekends. Pets by arrangement.*

Rooms	4 doubles, 3 twin/doubles: £110–£190. Extra bed/sofabed £30 p.p. per night.
Meals	Lunch from £6. Dinner, 3 courses, £25–£30.
Closed	Rarely.

Antonia & Stephen Bournes
The Globe Inn at Wells-next-the-Sea
The Buttlands,
Wells-Next-The-Sea, NR23 1EU

Tel	+44 (0)1328 710206
Email	hello@theglobeatwells.co.uk
Web	www.theglobeatwells.co.uk

Entry 126   Map 7

The Blakeney Hotel

The view here is matchless, a clean sweep across the salt marshes up to Blakeney Point. The estuary passes five paces from the front door and you can watch the boats slide by from a sun-trapping terrace, a convivial bar, a stylish restaurant and a beautiful first-floor sitting room that comes with binoculars to follow the local wildlife. Bedrooms have a contemporary country-house style: chic fabrics, cool colours, antique furniture, white linen on beautiful beds, sparkling bathrooms with posh oils. Many have views to the front, a couple have balconies, too. Elsewhere, you'll find three open fires, a bar for light lunches and local ales, an elegant drawing room where you can play Scrabble, read the papers, or dig into afternoon tea. There's an indoor pool with a gym, a steam room and a sauna, then glass doors onto the garden; you'll also find a games' room for children. Outside, paths lead down to the marshes, there are seals to spot, birds to watch, links golf at Sheringham and Cromer, a point to point at Fakenham. Sandringham is close, too. Dogs and children are very welcome. *Minimum stay: 2 nights at weekend.*

Rooms	19 doubles, 36 twin/doubles: £208–£386. 8 singles: £104–£193. Price includes dinner for 2
Meals	Lunch from £9.50. Dinner, 3 courses, included; non-residents £32.
Closed	Never.

Stannard Family
The Blakeney Hotel
The Quay, Blakeney, Holt, NR25 7NE
Tel   +44 (0)1263 740797
Email   reception@blakeneyhotel.co.uk
Web   www.blakeneyhotel.co.uk

Cley Windmill

The setting here is magical: rushes flutter in the salt marsh, raised paths lead off to the sea, a vast sky hangs overhead. The windmill, now with new sails, dates to 1713. It became a house in the 1920s, the family home of James Blunt no less. Square rooms are bigger, a couple have sofas, while round rooms in the tower are impossibly romantic (one is for mountaineers only!). Six rooms are in the mill and you really want to go for these, though the cottage is set up for self-catering and visiting dogs. Inside, you find the loveliest drawing room – low ceiling, open fire, stripped floorboards and a cute little window seat. Bedrooms have a chic feel with Farrow & Ball colours, beautiful fabrics, the odd claw-foot bath. Those in the tower (with compact shower rooms) get smaller as you rise, but the view improves with every step; there's a viewing platform halfway up for all. You eat in a pretty dining room, perhaps crab fishcakes, Norfolk Lamb, pear tarte tatin with cinnamon ice cream. But plans are afoot to build an orangery and when it's ready, you'll eat there surrounded by the walled garden. *Minimum stay: 2 nights.*

Rooms	6 doubles, 2 twin/doubles: £159–£219. 1 cottage for 4: £390 for 3 days; extra days £50–£130; £495–£625 per week. Children under 12 £30.
Meals	Dinner, 3 courses, £27.50–£32.50.
Closed	Christmas.

	Simon Whatling
	Cley Windmill
	The Quay, Cley, Holt, NR25 7RP
Tel	+44 (0)1263 740209
Email	info@cleywindmill.co.uk
Web	www.cleywindmill.co.uk

The Kings Head

This small Georgian inn was once the local jail. It is anything but these days, a quirky bolt hole full of creature comforts a few miles south of the North Norfolk coast. Outside, a large garden for barbecues in summer gives way to parkland beyond. Inside, cool interiors mix contemporary design and rustic bricks and mortar to great effect. You'll find cow-hide rugs, skis on the walls, Chesterfield sofas on original wood floors. There's a sitting-room bar for games in front of an open fire, then a restaurant with whitewashed walls and painted beams. Potter about and find cartwheel mirrors, lots of books, curious objects d'art. Bedrooms aren't huge, but nor is their price. You get lovely beds, smart fabrics, period colours, the odd antique; good showers wait in compact bathrooms. Downstairs, you'll find quiz nights, jazz nights and some lovely local food, perhaps corned beef hash with a quail's egg, local partridge with game chips, rhubarb and apple crumble; kids have their own menu, too. There's lots to do: cute villages, medieval Norwich, Fakenham for the races, the glorious north coast.

Rooms	4 doubles: £70–£130.
Meals	Lunch from £5.50.
	Dinner, 3 courses, £25–£30.
	Sunday lunch from £15.50.
Closed	Rarely.

Cliff Nye & Family
The Kings Head
Holt Road, Letheringsett,
Holt, NR25 7AR

Tel	+44 (0)1263 712691
Email	info@kingsheadnorfolk.co.uk
Web	www.kingsheadnorfolk.co.uk

Saracens Head

Lost in the lanes of deepest Norfolk, an English inn that's hard to match. Outside, Georgian red-brick walls stand to attention at the front, but nip round the back and find them at ease in a beautiful courtyard where you can knock back a pint of Wherry in the evening sun before slipping inside to eat. Tim and Janie upped sticks from the Alps, unable to resist the allure of this lovely old inn. A sympathetic refurbishment has worked its magic, but the spirit remains the same: this is a country-house pub with lovely staff who go the extra mile. Downstairs the bar hums with happy locals who come for Norfolk ales and good French wines, while the food in the restaurant is as good as ever: Norfolk pheasant and rabbit terrine, wild duck or Cromer crab, treacle tart and caramel ice-cream. Upstairs, there's a sitting room on the landing, then six pretty rooms. All have have smart carpets, wooden furniture, comfy beds and sparkling bathrooms. There's masses to do: ancient Norwich, the coast at Cromer, golf on the cliffs at Sheringham, Blickling Hall, a Jacobean pile. Don't miss Sunday lunch.

Rooms	5 twin/doubles: £110–£130.
	1 family room for 4: £110–£160.
	Singles £75. Extra bed/sofabed £25 per
	person per night.
Meals	Lunch from £6.50.
	Dinner, 3 courses, £25–£35.
Closed	Rarely.

Tim & Janie Elwes
Saracens Head
Wolterton,
Norwich, NR11 7LZ
Tel   +44 (0)1263 768909
Email   info@saracenshead-norfolk.co.uk
Web   www.saracenshead-norfolk.co.uk

The Pheasant Inn

A super little inn lost in beautiful country, the kind you hope to chance upon. The Kershaws run it with great passion and an instinctive understanding of its traditions. The bars are wonderful. Brass beer taps glow, 100-year old photos of the local community hang on stone walls, the clock above the fire keeps perfect time. Fires burn, bowler hats and saddles pop up here and there, varnished ceilings shine. House ales are expertly kept, Timothy Taylor's and Wylam waiting for thirsty souls. Fruit and vegetables come from the garden, while Robin's lovely food hits the spot perfectly, perhaps twice-baked cheese soufflé, slow-roasted Northumberland lamb, brioche and marmalade bread and butter pudding; as for Sunday lunch, *The Observer* voted it 'Best in the North'. Bedrooms in the old hay barn are light and airy, cute and cosy, great value for money. You're in the Northumberland National Park – no traffic jams, not too much hurry. You can sail on the lake, cycle round it or take to the hills and walk. For £10 you can also gaze into the universe at the Kielder Observatory (best in winter). Brilliant. *Minimum stay: 2 nights at weekends.*

Rooms	4 doubles, 3 twins: £95–£100. 1 family room for 4: £95–£140. Singles £65–£70. Dinner, B&B from £70 to £75 per person. Extra bed/sofabed £15 per person per night.
Meals	Bar meals from £9.95. Dinner, 3 courses, £20–£30. Sunday lunch from £11.50.
Closed	Christmas.

Walter, Irene & Robin Kershaw
The Pheasant Inn
Stannersburn,
Hexham, NE48 1DD
Tel   +44 (0)1434 240382
Email   stay@thepheasantinn.com
Web   www.thepheasantinn.com

Hart's Nottingham

A small enclave of good things. You're on the smart side of town at the end of a cul-de-sac, thus remarkably quiet. You're also at the top of the hill and close to the castle with views that sweep south for miles; at night, a carpet of light sparkles beneath you. Inside, cool lines and travertine marble greet you in reception. Smart bedrooms do the trick. They're not huge, but come with all the trimmings: wide-screen TVs, Bose sound systems, super little bathrooms, king-size beds wrapped in crisp white cotton. Those on the ground floor open onto the garden, each with a terrace where you can breakfast in good weather; rooms on higher floors have better views (six overlook the courtyard). There is a cool little bar, the hub of the hotel, but Hart's Restaurant across the courtyard serves breakfast and light bites, and offers excellent food: perhaps wild mushroom arancini, sea bream with lemon and hazelnut, quince soufflé with vanilla ice cream. There's lots to explore: the Lace Market, the city caves, Trent Bridge for the cricket (the England team stay here). There's a private car park for hotel guests, too.

Rooms	29 doubles: £139–£189.
	2 suites for 2: £279.
	1 family room for 4: £149–£206.
Meals	Continental breakfast £10; full English £15. Lunch, 2 courses £22. Dinner, 3 courses £32. Sunday lunch, 3 courses, £29.50.
Closed	Never.

Adam Worthington
Hart's Nottingham
Standard Hill, Park Row,
Nottingham, NG1 6GN

Tel	+44 (0)115 988 1900
Email	reception@hartshotel.co.uk
Web	www.hartsnottingham.co.uk

Langar Hall

Langar Hall is one of the loveliest places in this book, reason enough to come to Nottinghamshire. It sits at the top of a hardly noticeable hill in glorious parkland, bang next door to the church. The Skirving family arrived 160 years ago, building on the site of Admiral Lord Howe's burned-down home. Much of what fills the house arrived then and it's easy to feel intoxicated by statues and busts in the pillared dining room, ancient tomes overflowing from bookshelves, an eclectic collection of art. Lila – Imogen's granddaughter – is now in charge, and very much following in her grandmother's footsteps; Langar remains a quirky country house with charming staff and a touch of bohemian flair. Bedrooms are lovely, some resplendent with antiques, others with beautiful wallpapers or a grand four-poster. As for dinner, it's a big treat, perhaps wild turbot with mussels and dill, Belvoir pheasant with cider and thyme, rhubarb soufflé with ginger beer sorbet. There's a cocktail bar, a conservatory, a flower-filled terrace for afternoon tea in summer, then beautiful gardens that delight. One of a kind.

Rooms	7 doubles, 2 twins, 1 four-poster: £100-£199. 1 suite for 2: £160-£225. 1 chalet for 2: £100-£125. Singles £100-£160. Extra bed/sofabed £30 p.p. per night.
Meals	Lunch £18.50-£23.50. Dinner £30-£50. Sunday lunch £39.50.
Closed	Never.

Lila Skirving
Langar Hall
Church Lane, Langar,
Nottingham, NG13 9HG

Tel	+44 (0)1949 860559
Email	info@langarhall.co.uk
Web	www.langarhall.com

Old Bank Hotel

You're in the heart of old Oxford, with Merton College and Christ Church Meadow to the south, the Radcliffe Camera and the Bodleian Library to the north, and University College and the Botanic Gardens at Magdalen Bridge to the east. As for the Old Bank, its airy interiors are home to an exceptional collection of modern art and photography. The hub is the old tiller's hall, now a cocktail bar and brasserie, with six arched windows overlooking the high street. Food is on tap all day long, anything from a pizza or a steak to afternoon tea, with meat from the owner's farm and fish from the Channel Islands. Bedrooms are gorgeous: beautiful beds, pleated curtains, original art, robes in chic bathrooms. Some have sofas, others padded windows, you get flat-screen TVs and good WiFi throughout. There's a peaceful library bar for residents, a decked courtyard for breakfast in summer, then the rarest commodity in Oxford: free off-street parking. The University Church of St Mary stands opposite, so climb its tower for the best views of Oxford. The Ashmolean and Pitt Rivers Museums are close. *Minimum stay: 2 nights at weekends.*

Rooms	26 doubles, 14 twin/doubles: £215–£485. 2 suites for 3: £395–£560.
Meals	Breakfast £5–£15. Lunch & dinner £5–£30. Afternoon tea from £6.95.
Closed	Never.

Rebecca Mofford
Old Bank Hotel
92–94 High Street,
Oxford, OX1 4BJ

Tel	+44 (0)1865 799599
Email	info@oldbank-hotel.co.uk
Web	www.oldbank-hotel.co.uk

Turl Street Kitchen & Tower House Rooms

You land in the middle of Oxford at this quirky restaurant with rooms and find yourself surrounded by ancient colleges, with the Ashmolean Museum and the Bodleian Library both close. Interiors come in canteen style, with waitresses buzzing about, an open kitchen on display, a cool, shabby chic feel and happy chatter from people in for breakfast, lunch and dinner – this is a very popular community hub. Local food is sourced ethically and the menu changes twice a day, perhaps spiced carrot soup, steak and kidney pie, blood orange and vanilla cheesecake. There's WiFi throughout, the daily papers, a first-floor sitting room straight out of a student house. It's fun, easy going, a place for all. It's also a social enterprise, with profits going to charity, as they do 50 paces around the corner at Tower House Rooms, a terraced house with a difference: the old city wall runs through it with a 16th-century watch tower attached. Some rooms are small and share a bathroom, others are big, perhaps with a claw-foot bath. Expect good beds, smart colours, white linen, pretty throws. It's a peaceful spot, too.

Rooms	5 doubles; 3 doubles sharing 1 bathroom: £110–£170. Singles from £100. Cots available for children under 5 at no charge.
Meals	Lunch from £6.50. Dinner, 3 courses, £20–£25.
Closed	24 December – 2 January.

Charis Sharpe
Turl Street Kitchen & Tower House Rooms
15 Ship Street,
Oxford, OX1 3DA

Tel	+44 (0)1865 246828
Email	info@towerhouseoxford.co.uk
Web	www.towerhouseoxford.co.uk

Old Parsonage Hotel

The Old Parsonage has been at the centre of Oxford life for over 350 years. It stands in the middle of town on land owned by University College and was once home to Oscar Wilde. It is one of the loveliest places to stay in town, its beautiful interiors touching every corner. Chief among its virtues are its shaded dining terrace, its exceptional art collection, and its first-floor library (curated by Philip Blackwell), which opens onto a small roof terrace. Inside, flames flicker in an ancient fireplace, newspapers wait by mullioned windows, fresh flowers scent the air. The restaurant doubles as an art gallery, its charcoal walls crammed with portraits, a theatrical setting for a good meal, perhaps Devon crab, blanquette de veau, lemon tart with crème fraîche. Bedrooms come in pale greys with the best beds, the crispest linen, pretty throws and padded bedheads. Bigger rooms have sofas, some overlook the back garden, all have robes and spoiling oils and in beautiful marble bathrooms. The 'city of dreaming spires' is on your doorstep, there are bikes to borrow on which to explore. *Minimum stay: 2 nights at weekends.*

Rooms	22 doubles, 7 twins: £215-£485. 6 suites for 3: £395-£560.
Meals	Breakfast £5-£15. Lunch from £18. Dinner, 3 courses, £25-£45. Sunday lunch £25-£30. Afternoon tea £25.
Closed	Never.

Jeremy Mogford
Old Parsonage Hotel
1 Banbury Road,
Oxford, OX2 6NN

Tel	+44 (0)1865 310210
Email	reservations@oldparsonage-hotel.co.uk
Web	www.oldparsonage-hotel.co.uk

Artist Residence Oxford

Justin and Charlie's ability to create beautiful small hotels at the speed of light is unprecedented. Their fourth – lost in the country a few miles west of Oxford – is a reinvention of the country pub, though not as you might think. This isn't a stripped-back monument to contemporary design, rather a cool take on all things retro with quirky art and a little neon mixed in for good measure. You'll find vintage wallpapers, vivid colours, glass cabinets filled with curios, then a pink, up-cycled sofa in the cocktail bar. Country rugs cover flagstone floors, a fire burns on both sides in the bar, an original pine bench comes with plumped-up cushions. You eat in the restaurant amid ferns and flock wallpaper, perhaps Dorset crab with sorrel sauce, local venison with rainbow chard, gin and tonic panna cotta; there's a pie and a pint at the bar, too, and a dining terrace that overlooks the kitchen garden. Stunning bedrooms set the standard for others to follow: fat beds, exposed timbers, robes in flawless bathrooms, old tea chests for bedside tables. We've hardly scratched the surface. Exceptional. *Minimum stay: 2 nights at weekends.*

Rooms	5 doubles, 1 twin: £140–£290. 3 suites for 2: £180–£350. Extra beds £40 p.p. per night. Under 12s £30.
Meals	Lunch from £6.50. Dinner, 3 courses, about £40; 5-course tasting menu, £60. Sunday lunch from £15.95.
Closed	Never.

Charlie & Justin Salisbury
Artist Residence Oxford
Station Rd, South Leigh, Witney, OX29 6XN

Tel	+44 (0)1993 656220
Email	oxford@artistresidence.co.uk
Web	www.artistresidence.co.uk/ our-hotels/oxford/

The Feathers Hotel

Woodstock is the estate village to Blenheim Palace, one of Britain's finest houses, seat of the Dukes of Marlborough, birthplace of Winston Churchill. As for the hotel, it was once a draper's, then a butcher's, so it's no surprise it became a stylish hotel serving excellent food. In the morning you breakfast leisurely, then stroll up to the big house and spend the day dropping your jaw before coming home for afternoon tea in the courtyard. Inside, elegant, uncluttered interiors keep things simple: beautiful art, smouldering fires, a wall or two of original panelling, flowers everywhere. Ancient windows flood rooms with light, you find colourful rugs on wooden floors, then more gin than you can shake a stick at in the sitting-room bar (over 300 different bottles). Bedrooms have a contemporary feel with smart fabrics, lovely beds, mohair throws, delicate wallpapers. Some have sofas, all come with robes in fancy bathrooms. Back downstairs, delicious food waits in the restaurant, perhaps crab ravioli, loin of venison, treacle tart with blackberry sorbet. Bicester Village and Oxford are close. *Minimum stay: 2 nights at weekends in summer.*

Rooms	13 doubles, 3 twin/doubles: £99–£229. 5 suites for 2: £159–£319. Singles £99.
Meals	Lunch from £5. Bar meals from £10. Dinner £37.50–£45; 5-course tasting menu £55; not Sunday. Sunday lunch from £14.
Closed	Never.

Dominique Ghislane
The Feathers Hotel
Market Street,
Woodstock, OX20 1SX

Tel	+44 (0)1993 812291
Email	enquiries@feathers.co.uk
Web	www.feathers.co.uk

Entry 138   Map 3

The Swan

Free-range bantams strut in the garden, a pint of Hooky waits at the bar. This lovely old pub sits on the river Windrush with the village cricket pitch waiting beyond. It started life as a water mill and stands on the Devonshire estate, hence the pictures of the Mitford sisters that hang on the walls. Outside, wisteria wanders across golden stone and creepers blush red in the autumn sun. Interiors hit the spot: low ceilings, open fires, beautiful windows, stone walls. Over the years thirsty feet on their way to the bar have worn grooves into ancient flagstones (including those of prime ministers and French presidents). As for the food, seasonal menus brim with local produce, offering delicious delights, perhaps game terrine with pear chutney, roast partridge with a red wine jus, rhubarb and apple crumble. Bedrooms in the old forge have 15th-century walls and 21st-century interior design; those in the cottage across the lane are yards from the river. Expect crisp linen, comfy beds, warm colours and good art. Several have claw-foot baths, one has a pink chaise longue. Burford is close.

Rooms	4 doubles, 5 twin/doubles, 1 twin: £125-£150. 1 suite for 2: £195. Singles from £70.
Meals	Lunch from £5. Dinner, 3 courses, about £30. Sunday lunch from £14.95.
Closed	25-26 December.

Archie & Nicola Orr-Ewing
The Swan
Swinbrook,
Burford, OX18 4DY

Tel	+44 (0)1993 823339
Email	info@theswanswinbrook.co.uk
Web	www.theswanswinbrook.co.uk

The Shaven Crown

The Great Hall, with its spectacular roof, dates back to 1368 – quite some sitting room. It was built by monks from Bruern Abbey, reborn as a royal hunting lodge after the Dissolution of the Monasteries, then gifted to the village as an inn. Phil and Evelyn rescued it from neglect, then spent a year restoring long-lost glories – no mean feat. Potter about and find parquet flooring in the airy bar, books and armchairs in the pretty snug, then mullioned windows in the restaurant, where you dig into some lovely local food; rabbit rillettes with pear purée, loin of venison with a port wine sauce, espresso mousse with rum ice cream or a pear William cheesecake. In summer you spill out into a gorgeous courtyard for afternoon tea in the sun. Bedrooms have an elegant simplicity: airy colours, stylish fabrics, beautiful beds, sparkling bathrooms. One has a beamed roof, a couple are smaller, but have courtyard views. You're right in the heart of the Cotswolds, with Stratford for Shakespeare, Cheltenham for the races and Oxford for the spires all within easy reach. There's even jazz in the hall once a month. Dogs are very welcome.

Rooms	4 doubles, 3 twin/doubles: £95–£135.
Meals	Lunch from £6.50. Dinner, 3 courses, £25–£35. Sunday lunch from £17.95.
Closed	Rarely.

Phil & Evelyn Roberts
The Shaven Crown
High Street,
Shipton under Wychwood, OX7 6BA

Tel	+44 (0)1993 830500
Email	relax@theshavencrown.co.uk
Web	www.theshavencrown.co.uk

Entry 140   Map 3

The Feathered Nest Country Inn

The village is tiny, the view is fantastic, the bar is lively, the rooms are a treat. This 300-year-old malthouse sits in 55 acres of green and pleasant land and is utterly gorgeous inside and out. The view from the garden is one of the best in the Cotswolds – a five-mile sweep across quilted fields to a distant ridge. Interiors are just as good. A warm rustic style mixes beautifully with original timbers and old stone walls. A fire smoulders in the lovely bar, doors in the restaurant open onto the terrace, the garden room has tartan walls and the white wine cellar on display. Bedrooms delight. One is enormous, two have the view, beds are dressed in crisp linen. Some have power showers, one has a claw-foot bath, all have robes. You get coffee machines and iPod docks, too. Delicious food waits downstairs, perhaps octopus with lemon and garlic, pollock with saffron and fennel, tarte tatin with vanilla ice cream. You eat on the terrace in summer looking out on the lake and distant farms. A couple of luxurious cabins are soon to be sprinkled across the grounds – Amanda and Tony do nothing by halves. Magical. *Minimum stay: 2 nights at weekends.*

Rooms	4 doubles: £245–£295. Dinner, B&B £185–£205 p.p.
Meals	Lunch, 3 courses, £38. Dinner, 4 courses, £65; 6 courses, £95.
Closed	Monday to Wednesday.

Tony & Amanda Timmer
The Feathered Nest Country Inn
Nether Westcote,
Chipping Norton, OX7 6SD

Tel	+44 (0)1993 833030
Email	reservations@thefeatherednestinn.co.uk
Web	www.thefeatherednestinn.co.uk

The Kings Head Inn

A beautiful English inn, a 17th-century cider house made of ancient stone that sits on the green in a Cotswold village with free-range hens strutting their stuff and a family of ducks bathing in the pond. Inside, locals gather to chew the cud, scoff great food and wash it down with Cotswold ales. The fire burns all year, you get low ceilings, painted stone walls, the odd settle, country rugs on flagstone floors. Nicely priced bedrooms have lots of colour and style. Those in the main house have more character, those in the courtyard are bigger (and quieter). You'll find painted wood, pretty fabrics, rustic furniture, spotless bathrooms; most have great views, too. Breakfast and supper are taken in a pretty dining room (exposed stone walls, pale wood tables), while you can lunch by the fire in the bar on devilled kidneys, grilled mackerel, a plate of British cheeses. There are lovely unpompous touches like jugs of cow parsley in the loo. There's loads to do, too: antiques in Stow, golf at Burford, circular walks through gorgeous country. The front terrace teems with life in summer. *Minimum stay: 2 nights at weekends.*

Rooms	9 doubles, 3 twin/doubles: £100–£135. Singles £80–£100.
Meals	Lunch from £7.50. Dinner, 3 courses, about £30. Sunday lunch £15.
Closed	25-27 December.

Archie & Nicola Orr-Ewing
The Kings Head Inn
The Green, Bledington,
Chipping Norton, OX7 6XQ
Tel   +44 (0)1608 658365
Email   info@kingsheadinn.net
Web   www.kingsheadinn.net

Hambleton Hall Hotel & Restaurant

Hambleton is matchless, one of the seven wonders of English country-house hotels. It sits on a tiny peninsular that juts into Rutland Water. You can sail on it, cycle round it, or watch terns and osprey commute across it. Back at the house the undisputed wonders of Hambleton wait: sofas by the fire in the panelled hall, a pillared bar in red for cocktails, a Michelin star in the elegant dining room. French windows in the sitting room – beautiful art, fresh flowers, the daily papers – open onto fine gardens. Expect clipped lawns and gravel paths, a formal parterre garden that bursts with summer colour and a walled swimming pool with views over parkland to the water. Bedrooms are flawless: hand-stitched Italian linen, mirrored armoires, Roberts radios and marble bathrooms. Stefa's eye for fabrics, some of which coat the walls, is impeccable; the Pavilion, a two-bedroom suite, has its own terrace. Polish the day off with ambrosial food, perhaps beetroot terrine with horseradish sorbet, fallow venison with Asian pear, passion fruit soufflé with banana sorbet. Barnsdale Gardens are close. *Minimum stay: 2 nights at weekends.*

Rooms	15 twin/doubles: £290–£725. 1 suite for 4: £510–£725. Singles £200–£220. Dinner, B&B £210 per person. Extra bed/sofabed £35 per person per night.
Meals	Lunch from £29. Dinner, 3 courses, £73; tasting menu £92. Sunday lunch £58.
Closed	Never.

Tim & Stefa Hart
Hambleton Hall Hotel & Restaurant
Ketton Road, Hambleton,
Oakham, LE15 8TH

Tel	+44 (0)1572 756991
Email	hotel@hambletonhall.com
Web	www.hambletonhall.com

The Olive Branch

A lovely pub in a sleepy Rutland village, where bridle paths lead out across peaceful fields. It dates to the 17th century and is built of Clipsham stone, as is York Minster. Inside, a warm, informal, rustic chic hits the spot perfectly with open fires, old beams, stone walls and choir stalls in the bar. But there's more here than cool design. This is a place to come and eat great food, the lovely, local seasonal stuff that's cooked with passion by Sean and his brigade, perhaps potted pork and stilton with apple jelly, haunch of venison with a juniper fondant, then a boozy rhubarb trifle. Bedrooms in Beech House across the lane are gorgeous. Three have terraces, one has a free-standing bath, all come with crisp linen, pretty beds, Roberts radios and real coffee. Super breakfasts — smoothies, boiled eggs and soldiers, the full cooked works — are served in a stone-walled barn with flames leaping in the wood-burner. The front garden fills in summer, the sloe gin comes from local berries, and Newark is close for the biggest antiques market in Europe. Picnic hampers can be arranged. A total gem.

Rooms	5 doubles: £115–£205. 1 family room for 4: £115–£255. Singles from £97.50. Extra beds £30.
Meals	Lunch from £8.50. Dinner, 3 courses, £28.50–£40. Sunday lunch from £24.50.
Closed	Rarely.

Ben Jones & Sean Hope
The Olive Branch
Main Street, Clipsham,
Oakham, LE15 7SH

Tel   +44 (0)1780 410355
Email   info@theolivebranchpub.com
Web   www.theolivebranchpub.com

Old Downton Lodge

The last time anything really happened here was in 1067 when Edric the Wild got a bit shirty with invading Normans. Fast forward five hundred years and Old Downton is taking shape. It's a fine old building, a little like walking onto the set of Wolf Hall, with original timbers, mighty crossbeams and beautiful stone walls. It sits in pristine country. Pheasants strut, hills roll, woodlands sprawl along distant ridges; a stunning walk across it all takes you over to Ludlow. Back at the house Pippa and Willem look after you in great style. There's a lovely sitting room in the old dairy with a roaring fire, then a dining room in an 11th-century barn that resembles a medieval banqueting hall. In summer, life moves into the courtyard where you can eat, drink and make merry. Big bedrooms mix timber frames, stone walls, flagged floors and oak furniture, while bathrooms have robes and lashings of hot water. Back outside, follow the river Teme up to Downton Gorge for ferns, otters, Roman baths and bluebells in spring. Bring your Tesla — there are two chargers here. *Pets by arrangement.*

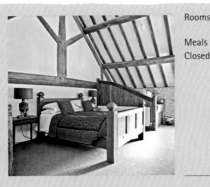

Rooms	5 doubles, 2 twins, 2 four-posters: £155-£295. Singles £145-£295.
Meals	Dinner, 3-9 courses, from £50.
Closed	Christmas.

Willem & Pippa Vlok
Old Downton Lodge
Downton-on-the-Rock,
Ludlow, SY8 2HU

Tel	+44 (0)1568 771826
Email	bookings@olddowntonlodge.com
Web	www.olddowntonlodge.com

The Castle Hotel

This thriving medieval market town sits amid some of the loveliest country in the land, a launch pad for walkers and cyclists alike, with Offa's Dyke, Long Mynd and the Kerry Ridgeway all close. After a day in the hills, roll back to this quirky hotel for a night of gentle carousing. You'll find heaps of country comforts: hearty food, impeccable ales, super rooms with honest prices. Downstairs, there's a coal fire in the pretty snug, oak panelling in the breakfast room, and Millie the short-haired dachshund who patrols the corridors with aplomb. Stylish bedrooms upstairs have all been refurbished. Expect good beds, warm colours, flat-screen TVs, an armchair if there's room. Some are up in the eaves, several have views of the Shropshire hills, two have baths in the room. Back downstairs you find the sort of food you'd want after a day in the hills, perhaps hot garlic prawns, beef and ale pie, sticky toffee pudding. Don't miss the hugely popular real ale festival in July, the beer drinker's equivalent of Glastonbury. The garden terrace, with long country views, is a fine spot for a sundowner.

Rooms	9 doubles, 1 twin: £95-£150. 2 family rooms for 4: £130-£155. Singles from £75. Dinner, B&B from £82.50 p.p. Extra beds for children £20.
Meals	Lunch from £4.50. Dinner, 3 courses, about £25.
Closed	Rarely.

Henry & Rebecca Hunter
The Castle Hotel
Bishops Castle, SY9 5BN

Tel	+44 (0)1588 638403
Email	stay@thecastlehotelbishopscastle.co.uk
Web	www.thecastlehotelbishopscastle.co.uk

The Haughmond

This is one of those lovely places that sits in beautiful country, serves delicious food and looks after guests without the slightest hint of pomposity. It's an 18th-century inn that doubles as a hub for village life, and it comes with a small shop full of local produce. It ticks to its own beat, locals pop in to chat, cyclists and walkers drop in for coffee, dogs are very welcome. The big draw is Martin's food and the restaurant is busy for lunch and dinner most days, no mean feat for a country inn. Whatever can be is sourced locally and the seven-course tasting menu is a steal; highlights include mackerel with cucumber, beef with horseradish, a sinful pistachio soufflé. You can walk it all off from the front door; the place takes its name from a nearby hill, where big views wait at the top. Back at the inn, spotless rooms are both warmly stylish and nicely priced. A couple are bigger, all have comfy beds, crisp linen and good bathrooms. One has a Juliet balcony, those at the back have country views, all have fresh flowers, local art and smart TVs. Shrewsbury is close. An affordable treat.

Rooms	2 doubles, 3 twin/doubles: £90–£120. Singles from £80. Extra bed £10.
Meals	Lunch from £8; Tues-Sat. Dinner, 3 courses, about £30; tasting menu, 7 courses, £40; not Sun. Sunday lunch £16–£20.
Closed	Christmas & New Year.

Martin & Mel Broad
The Haughmond
Upton Magna,
Shrewsbury, SY4 4TZ
Tel   +44 (0)1743 709918
Email   contact@thehaughmond.co.uk
Web   www.thehaughmond.co.uk

Meeson Hall

Sitting in eight acres of lawns and woodland with open country all around, this lovely country house dates back to 1640 and is a treasure trove of beautiful things – the Jacobean chimney piece in the dining room is one of the finest in the land. Guests have the run of the ground floor: a grandly panelled hall with a crackling fire, an airy drawing room for afternoon tea and a library filled with original art. You eat communally in the splendid dining room, merrily digging into Mark's lovely home cooking – perhaps pâté with redcurrant jelly, a Barnsley chop with a red wine jus, followed by bread and butter pudding. Bedrooms come in smart country-house style: warm colours, smartly dressed beds, antique furniture, fresh flowers. There are sofas, silver teapots, perhaps a chandelier, then robes and the odd claw-foot bath in wallpapered bathrooms. Outside, chickens provide eggs for breakfast and bluebells run riot in spring. All of which would be blossom in the wind without Adrian and Mark, who go out of their way to make your stay here special. Ironbridge, birthplace of the Industrial Revolution, is close. *Over 16s welcome.*

Rooms	4 doubles: £165-£215. 1 suite for 4: £180-£320. Singles from £145.
Meals	Lunch from £10. Dinner, 3 courses, £30. Sunday lunch £25. Afternoon tea from £10.
Closed	Rarely.

Adrian Jones & Mark Scarrott
Meeson Hall
Meeson, TF6 6PG

Tel	+44 (0)1952 541262
Email	enquiries@meesonhall.co.uk
Web	www.meesonhall.co.uk

Sebastians

This cute little restaurant with rooms occupies an old merchant's house that dates from 1640. Michelle and Mark have been at the helm for some 25 years cooking up a fine reputation – not only for their delicious food, but for the quirky, old-world interiors in which they serve it. Inside you find huge beams, timber frames, half panelling and stripped floors. Big warm colours sit on the walls, smartly clothed tables are lit by candles, deco posters of the Orient Express hang in every room (Mark supplies the train with canapés and desserts). Back in the restaurant, sofas wait in front of a fire that smoulders from morning to night in winter. Here you drool over the menu before digging into delicious food, perhaps scallop ravioli with lemon grass and ginger, short rib of beef in a red wine sauce, dark chocolate mousse with honey ice cream. Six nicely-priced rooms wait, two in the main house (timber frames, lots of colour), four off the attractive courtyard (comfy sofas, lovely bathrooms). Plans are afoot for a couple of suites. Welsh hills wait to the west, so bring your walking boots.

Rooms	5 doubles, 1 twin/double: £85–£95. Singles £75–£85.
Meals	Breakfast £6.95–£11.95. Dinner, Weds & Thurs, £28–£44.50; Fri & Sat, 5 courses, £44.50. Restaurant closed Sun, Mon & Tues.
Closed	Rarely.

Michelle & Mark Sebastian Fisher
Sebastians
45 Willow Street,
Oswestry, SY11 1AQ

Tel	+44 (0)1691 655444
Email	info@sebastians-hotel.com
Web	www.sebastians-hotel.com

Pen-y-Dyffryn Country Hotel

In a blissful valley lost to the world, a small country house that sparkles on the side of a peaceful hill. This is one of those lovely places where guests return again and again, mostly due to Audrey and Miles, who run a very happy ship. Outside, fields tumble down to a stream that marks the border with Wales. Daffodils erupt in spring, the lawns are scattered with deckchairs in summer, paths lead into the hills for fine walking. Lovely interiors are just the ticket: Laura Ashley wallpaper and an open fire in the quirky bar; colourful art and super food in the pretty restaurant; the daily papers and the odd chaise longue in the sitting room. Bedrooms hit the spot. Most have the view, one has a French sleigh bed, a couple have jacuzzi baths for two. Four lovely rooms outside are dog-friendly and have their own patios. You get warm colours, crisp linen, pretty fabrics and sparkling bathrooms. After a day in the hills come back for a good dinner, perhaps wild mushroom risotto, pan-fried wood pigeon, hot chocolate fondant with vanilla ice-cream. Offa's Dyke and Powis Castle are close. *Minimum stay: 2 nights at weekends.*

Rooms	8 doubles, 4 twins: £120-£190. Singles £90-£99. Dinner, B&B £99-£136 per person. Extra bed/sofabed £35 per person per night.
Meals	Light lunch for residents, by arrangement. Dinner £30-£37.
Closed	Rarely.

Miles & Audrey Hunter
Pen-y-Dyffryn Country Hotel
Rhydycroesau,
Oswestry, SY10 7JD

Tel	+44 (0)1691 653700
Email	stay@peny.co.uk
Web	www.peny.co.uk

The Talbot Inn at Mells

The Talbot is an absolute stunner, one of the loveliest inns in the land. It sits in a timeless village lost in a tangle of country lanes, a 15th-century coaching inn reborn for the 21st-century. Sweep under the carriage arch and you enter a cobbled courtyard, where life gathers in good weather. There's a tithe-barn sitting room with big sofas and a Sunday cinema, then the Coach House Grill, where you eat at weekends under hanging beams. As for the main house, weave along ancient passageways and find stone walls, rugs on wood floors, crackling log fires and a low-ceilinged bar for a pint of Butcombe. The restaurant has colonised several cosy rooms and delicious food flies from the kitchen, perhaps white onion and cider soup, monkfish and mussel stew, chocolate and salted caramel sundae. Bedrooms are the best, some smaller, others huge with claw-foot baths, walk-in showers and modern four-posters. Add lovely staff to the mix and you have a slice of heaven. There's a colourful garden and great local walking, so bring your boots. The First World War poet, Siegfried Sassoon, is buried in the churchyard.

Rooms	8 doubles: £100–£160.
Meals	Lunch & dinner £5–£30.
	Sunday lunch from £15.
Closed	Rarely.

Matt Greenlees
The Talbot Inn at Mells
Selwood Street, Mells,
Frome, BA11 3PN

Tel	+44 (0)1373 812254
Email	info@talbotinn.com
Web	www.talbotinn.com

The Pilgrims Restaurant with Rooms

Medieval pilgrims in search of King Arthur's tomb would stop here for sustenance before heading out across the marshes on their way to Glastonbury Abbey. These days, the food, the welcome and the rooms are all so lovely you're more likely to suffer a crisis of faith and stay put. Jools is to blame – his food is far too good to miss, good enough to alter the DNA of these walls – the Pilgrims is not an inn these days, but a restaurant with rooms. All the lovely old stuff survives – stone walls, timber frames, panelled walls and a couple of sofas in front of the fire. Tables in the restaurant are nicely spaced apart with subtle lighting and service that hits the spot. As for the food, expect local ingredients cooked to perfection, perhaps Lyme Bay scallops, rack of lamb, smooth dark chocolate pot with a hint of stem ginger. Five lovely bedrooms wait in the old skittle alley. Three have cathedral ceilings, all come with exposed stone walls, flat-screen TVs and crisp linen on good beds. As for the bathrooms, expect double-ended baths, separate power showers, fluffy robes. Wells and Glastonbury are close.

Rooms	4 doubles, 1 twin/double: £100–£130. Singles £80–£130.
Meals	Lunch from £8. Dinner, 3 courses, about £30. Restaurant closed Sunday to Thursday.
Closed	Rarely.

Julian & Sally Mitchison
The Pilgrims Restaurant with Rooms
Lovington, Castle Cary, BA7 7PT
Tel   +44 (0)1963 240597
Email   jools@pilgrimsrestaurant.co.uk
Web   www.pilgrimsrestaurant.co.uk

The White Hart

Cool inns with lovely rooms in interesting parts of the land are a big hit with lots of us – we like the easy style, the local food, the good prices and the happy staff. The White Hart is a case in point, a beautifully refurbished inn. It sits on Somerton's ancient market square, 16th-century bricks and mortar, 21st-century lipstick and pearls. Inside, old and new mix beautifully: stone walls and parquet flooring, lovely sofas in front of the fire, funky lamps hanging above the bar. You'll find soft colours, padded window seats, country rugs, antler chandeliers. There's a cute booth in a stone turret, then lovely food waits, perhaps a chargrilled steak, Cornish crab cakes or wood-roasted pork loin. In summer, you spill onto a smart courtyard or into the garden for views of open country. Upstairs, fabulous bedrooms await. You might find timber frames, a claw-foot bath, a wall of paper or stripped boards. All have super beds, flat-screen TVs, lovely bathrooms and a nice price. Beautiful Somerset is all around, don't miss it.

Rooms	8 doubles: £85–£115.
	Dogs £10 per night.
Meals	Lunch from £6.
	Dinner, 3 courses, £25–£30.
	Sunday lunch from £15.
Closed	Never.

Abbie Windust
The White Hart
Market Place,
Somerton, TA11 7LX

Tel	+44 (0)1458 272273
Email	info@whitehartsomerton.com
Web	www.whitehartsomerton.com

The Devonshire Arms

What makes a great little inn these days? The Devonshire Arms has all the ingredients: lots of style, good prices, a community feel, some lovely rooms. It's in the right place, too, bang on the village green, with a terrace at the front, a garden at the back and a courtyard in between. Inside, is just as good. This isn't one of those places where every table is laid up for food; on the contrary, the best seats in the house are in the bar – a couple of armchairs in front of the fire. Step inside and find stylish interiors throughout. You get painted panelling in the restaurant – a sort of contemporary take on an 18th-century gentleman's club – then cool colours in the bar, where you can grab a pint of Butcombe, then spin outside to watch village life pass by. Lovely rooms have terrific prices. You'll find good beds, white linen, pretty furniture and excellent bathrooms; one has a free-standing bath. Elsewhere, red leather banquettes, fresh flowers, kind staff, the daily papers. As for the food, it's just the ticket: local partridge, fillet of bream, treacle tart with buttermilk ice cream.

Rooms	8 doubles, 1 twin/double: £95–£140. Singles from £85. Extra bed/sofabed £20 p.p.p.n.
Meals	Lunch from £5.95. Dinner, 3 courses, about £30. Sunday lunch from £12.95.
Closed	25–26 December.

Philip & Sheila Mepham
The Devonshire Arms
Long Sutton,
Langport, TA10 9LP

Tel	+44 (0)1458 241271
Email	mail@thedevonshirearms.com
Web	www.thedevonshirearms.com

Little Barwick House

A beautiful restaurant with rooms lost in peaceful lanes south of Yeovil. Tim and Emma rolled west 14 years ago and now have a legion of fans who come to feast on their ambrosial food. Their small Georgian country house stands privately in three acres of peace. Horses graze in the paddock below, afternoon tea is served in the garden to the sound of birdsong in summer. Inside, chic interiors flood with light thanks to fine windows that run along the front. There's an open fire in the bar, eclectic reading in the sitting room, then contemporary art in the high-ceilinged dining room. Gorgeous bedrooms have a country-house feel and come with warm colours, pretty fabrics, Roberts radios, a sofa if there's room. You'll find fresh garden flowers, antique furniture, and White Company oils in compact bathrooms. Dinner is the main event, heaven in three courses. Everything is homemade and cooked by Tim and Emma, an equal partnership in the kitchen – perhaps Lyme Bay scallops, saddle of wild venison, dark chocolate tort with armagnac ice-cream. Posh wines by the glass come courtesy of clever technology. *Children over 5 welcome.*

Rooms	4 doubles, 2 twins: £100–£170. Singles from £75. Dinner, B&B £105–£130 per person. Extra bed/sofabed £25 per person per night.
Meals	Lunch, 2-3 courses, £25.95–£29.95; not Tues. Dinner, 2-3 courses, £41.95–£47.95.
Closed	Sunday nights & Mondays.

Emma & Tim Ford
Little Barwick House
Rexes Hollow Lane, Barwick,
Yeovil, BA22 9TD

Tel	+44 (0)1935 423902
Email	info@littlebarwick.co.uk
Web	www.littlebarwickhouse.co.uk

Lord Poulett Arms

An idyllic inn that's hard to beat. It's like stepping onto the pages of a Jane Austen novel. A clipped country elegance runs throughout – old stone walls and period colours, then noble portraits on the walls and beautiful old settles to take the strain. There are drawbacks – sooner or later you will have to leave, probably with a touch of envy for the locals. Smart rusticity abounds. A fire burns on both sides in the dining room, where you eat under beams at antique tables. You'll find the daily papers, sofas in the locals' bar, a pile of logs at the back door, then an informal French garden with a piste for boules. Bedrooms upstairs have a lovely style with fancy flock wallpaper, pretty fabrics and fresh flowers, perhaps a small chandelier or a carved wooden bed. Two rooms have slipper baths in the room; two have claw-foot baths in bathrooms one step across the landing; the suite is enormous and has an open fire. The food is just as lovely, perhaps pea and ham soup, confit pork belly, praline fondant with coffee ice cream. Don't miss Sunday lunch or summer barbecues. An affordable treat.

Rooms	2 doubles; 2 doubles with separate bath: £85–£95. 1 suite for 3: £100–£150. Singles from £60.
Meals	Lunch from £5. Dinner, 3 courses, £20–£35. Sunday lunch £18–£21.
Closed	Never.

Reservations Team
Lord Poulett Arms
High Street,
Hinton St George, TA17 8SE

Tel	+44 (0)1460 73149
Email	reservations@lordpoulettarms.com
Web	www.lordpoulettarms.com

The Swan

The Swan is gorgeous, a contemporary take on a village local. It's part of a new wave of pubs that open all day and do so much more than serve a good pint. The locals love it. They come for breakfast, pop in to buy a loaf of bread, then return for afternoon tea and raid the cake stands. It's right on the bustling street, with a sprinkling of tables and chairs on the pavement in French-café style. Interiors mix old and new brilliantly. You get Farrow & Ball colours and cool lamps hanging above the bar, then lovely old rugs on boarded floors and a wood-burner to keep things toasty. Push inland to find an airy restaurant open to the rafters that overlooks the garden. Here you dig into Tom Blake's fabulous food (he's ex-River Cottage), anything from grilled Cornish herring to a three-course feast, maybe crispy Lyme Bay cuttlefish, slow cooked Quantock venison, chocolate and salted caramel tart. Bedrooms are lovely. Two have fancy baths in the room, you get vintage French furniture, iPod docks, colourful throws and walk-in power showers. Glastonbury is close, as are the Mendips.

Rooms	5 doubles, 2 twin/doubles: £85–£135. Extra bed £20. Cots available. Dogs £10 per night.
Meals	Lunch from £5. Dinner, 3 courses, about £25. Sunday lunch from £14. Bar meals only Sun evening.
Closed	Rarely.

Sofie Baugh
The Swan
Cheddar Road,
Wedmore, BS28 4EQ
Tel   +44 (0)1934 710337
Email   s.baugh@theswanwedmore.com
Web   www.theswanwedmore.com

Swain House

Watchet is a sleepy town on the West Somerset coast, and while its day may have passed, its medieval harbour that once made it rich inspired Coleridge to write his famous poem 'The Rime of The Ancient Mariner'. As for this stylish B&B, it makes a great little base for gentle explorations – you'll find excellent hill walking, beaches, the coastal path, even a music festival in August. Once an antiques shop, it sits on the colourful, main street in town with a big window looking out onto the world. Downstairs, there's a stylish dining room that doubles as a sitting room, with a sofa in front of a fire and hanging lamps at the breakfast table. Upstairs, lovely rooms wait, the sort you expect to find in a boutique inn. You get a huge noble portrait covering one wall, then pretty armchairs, smart fabrics, padded bedheads and old-style radiators. Excellent bathrooms have walk-in showers, free-standing baths, robes and REN oils – exactly what you want after a day in the hills. Pub grub waits in town, posher nosh is a little further afield. The nearby car park is nicely priced, too.

Rooms	4 doubles: £135. Singles from £115.
Meals	Restaurants in village.
Closed	Rarely.

Jason & Annie Robinson
Swain House
48 Swain Street,
Watchet, TA23 0AG

Tel   +44 (0)1984 631038
Email   stay@swain-house.com
Web   www.swain-house.com

Luttrell Arms

You get a triple whammy here: spectacular Dunster Castle, its beautiful estate village and this medieval coaching inn on the high street — the view from the terrace across to the castle is candy for your eyes. Inside, a recent refurbishment has brought in a warm style. You'll find a beautiful restaurant with papered walls, an attractive sitting room for afternoon tea, an open fire in the high-ceilinged bar, then a boot bar for sleeping dogs and a game of cribbage. There are a couple of terraces for lunch in the sun, sofas on a veranda that overlooks a tiny courtyard. Bedrooms are scattered about, some with village views, others overlooking the estate. Four are huge with grand four-posters, two sitting under a 500-year-old hammer beam roof. Others have period furniture, pretty wallpapers, perhaps a small private terrace; simpler rooms are smaller, but have good beds. Tasty food spans the spectrum, perhaps a posh burger in the bar to smoked haddock chowder, braised shin of beef and chocolate and raspberry tart in the restaurant. Cliff tops and wild moors wait for fabulous walking. *Minimum stay: 2 nights at weekends*

Rooms	4 doubles, 20 twin/doubles, 4 four-posters: £110-£220. Singles £90-£100.
Meals	Lunch from £4.95. Bar meals from £10.95. Dinner, 3 courses, about £30. Sunday lunch from £15.95. Afternoon tea £12.95.
Closed	Rarely.

Becca Way
Luttrell Arms
36 High Street, Dunster, TA24 6SG
Tel   +44 (0)1643 821555
Email   enquiry@luttrellarms.co.uk
Web   www.luttrellarms.co.uk

Cross Lane House

Exmoor National Park wraps itself around this hotel, which sits in glorious countryside. Roy and Gaynor supply maps for gentle rambles and invigorating hikes from the door: an hour's walk along the rugged coastal path takes you down to Porlock Weir which teems with wildlife and birds. Return for afternoon tea in the medieval courtyard on sunny days: west country clotted cream, homemade scones, champagne if you want. On chillier days take tea round the roaring fire. Dinner is a relaxed affair with a hand picked wine list and the best of local produce. The Luttrell Arms (six miles) is good. Sleep deeply in peaceful bedrooms; there are four, each with a smart en suite. Fill up with big breakfasts served in the dining room before another day exploring Exmoor. Dunster Castle is six miles — there are plenty of challenging and gentle cycle routes, and a barn for storing muddy gear and bikes. *Minimum stay: 2 nights at weekends during high season, however please contact owner for availability.*

Rooms	3 doubles: £135-£190.
	1 suite for 3: £185-£215.
	Dinner, B&B £105-£137 p.p.
Meals	Dinner £29.50-£37.
	Afternoon tea £22.50.
Closed	Rarely.

Roy Butlin & Gaynor Smith
Cross Lane House
Allerford, Minehead, TA24 8HW
Tel   +44 (0)1643 863276
Email   info@crosslanehouse.com
Web   www.crosslanehouse.com

The Anchor

The Anchor is one of those lovely places that has resisted the urge to be precious. This is a cool little seaside inn where relaxed informality reigns; kids are welcome, staff are friendly, dogs fall asleep in the bar. You're 500 yards from the sea with a terrace that fills with locals in summer and lawns that run off towards the water. Inside, beautiful simplicity abounds – Cape Cod meets English country local. You get books everywhere, beautiful art, roaring fires, a happy vibe. The big draw is Sophie's lovely food. Game and venison come from local estates, fish and seafood from nearby waters, samphire and sea kale are foraged along the coast. Bedrooms fit the mood perfectly. Those in the house are warm and homely; garden rooms are big and airy with sofas inside and terraces that overlook nearby dunes. Don't miss dinner, perhaps fish soup, game ravioli, chocolate fondant with caramel ice cream. You wash it all down with Mark's legendary collection of bottled beers and fancy wines. There are festivals by the score – don't miss Latitude or Folk East. Starry skies amaze. Unmissable. *Minimum stay: 2 nights at weekends & in high season. Pets by arrangement.*

Rooms	10 doubles: £105–£165. Singles £85–£100. Extra bed/sofabed £20–£30 per person per night.
Meals	Lunch from £5.25. Dinner, 3 courses, about £30. Sunday lunch, 2 courses, £20.
Closed	Rarely.

Mark & Sophie Dorber
The Anchor
Main Street, Walberswick,
Southwold, IP18 6UA

Tel	+44 (0)1502 722112
Email	info@anchoratwalberswick.com
Web	www.anchoratwalberswick.com

The Westleton Crown

This is one of England's oldest coaching inns, with 800 years of continuous service under its belt. It stands in a village two miles inland from the sea at Dunwich, with Westleton Heath running east towards Minsmere RSPB Nature Reserve. Inside, stripped floors, smouldering fires, exposed brickwork and ancient beams sweep you back in time. Weave about and find nooks and crannies in which to hide, flames flickering in open fires, a huge map on the wall for walkers. You breakfast in the conservatory amid big photos of local landscapes; in summer doors open onto a terraced garden for barbecues in the sun. Fish comes straight off the boats at Lowestoft, local butchers provide local meat, so try slow-cooked Blythburgh pork belly, roasted hake fillet with crushed new potatoes or dark chocolate fondant with pistachio ice cream. Bedrooms are scattered about (Will and Kate loved theirs), some in the main house, others in converted stables. Expect off-whites, comfy beds, crisp linen, smart TVs. Bathrooms come courtesy of Fired Earth, some with claw-foot baths. Aldeburgh and Southwold are close. *Minimum stay: 2 nights at weekends.*

Rooms	26 doubles, 2 twins: £140–£205. 3 suites for 2: £215. 2 family rooms for 4: £180–£215. 1 single: £100. Extra beds £15–£25 p.p.
Meals	Lunch from £5.50. Dinner, 3 courses, £25–£35. Sunday lunch £19.95–£24.95
Closed	Never.

Gareth Clarke
The Westleton Crown
The Street, Westleton,
Saxmundham, IP17 3AD

Tel	+44 (0)1728 648777
Email	info@westletoncrown.co.uk
Web	www.westletoncrown.co.uk

Wentworth Hotel

The Wentworth has the loveliest position in town, the beach literally a pebble's throw from the garden, the sea rolling east under a vast sky. Inside, fires smoulder, clocks chime and seaside elegance abounds. It's all terrifically English, with vintage wallpapers, kind local staff and an elegant bar that opens onto a terrace garden. The restaurant looks out to sea, spilling onto a sunken terrace in summer for views of passing boats. Proper English fare is the order of the day: stilton soup, breast of guinea fowl, lemon posset with raspberries and shortbread. The hotel has been in the same family since 1920 and old-fashioned values mix harmoniously with interiors that are refreshed often to keep things sparkling. Airy bedrooms are deeply comfy, those at the front have sea views (and binoculars). Expect warm colours, smart fabrics, padded headboards and good beds; all have stylish bathrooms, too. You'll find sofas galore in the sitting rooms, but you may want to spurn them to walk by the sea. Joyce Grenfell was a regular. The Snape Maltings are close. *Minimum stay: 2 nights at weekends.*

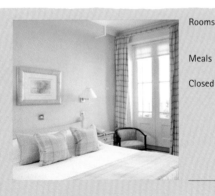

Rooms	7 doubles, 24 twin/doubles: £140-£220.
	4 singles: £85-£119.
	Dinner, B&B from £83 p.p.
Meals	Lunch from £5.
	Dinner, 2-3 courses, £21-£26.50.
Closed	Never.

Michael Pritt
Wentworth Hotel
Wentworth Road, Aldeburgh, IP15 5BD
Tel   +44 (0)1728 452312
Email   stay@wentworth-aldeburgh.com
Web   www.wentworth-aldeburgh.com

The Crown & Castle

A great place to wash up for a few lazy days. Orford is hard to beat, a sleepy Suffolk village blissfully marooned at the end of the road. River, beach and forest wait, as does the Crown & Castle, a welcoming English hostelry where the art of hospitality is practised with unstinting flair. The inn stands in the shadow of Orford's 12th-century castle. Uncluttered interiors have a warm, airy feel with stripped floorboards, open fires, wonderful art and flickering candles at night. Chic bedrooms have Vi-Spring beds, fancy bathrooms, lovely fabrics, the odd armchair. Four in the main house have watery views, the suite is huge, the garden rooms big and light, the courtyard rooms a real delight. All have crisp white linen, TVs, DVDs and digital radios. Wellington boots wait at the back door, so pull on a pair and explore Rendlesham Forest or hop on a boat and chug over to Orfordness. Ambrosial food awaits your return, perhaps potted brown shrimps, a faultless steak and kidney pie, crushed pistachio meringue with a chocolate ice-cream sundae. Sutton Hoo is close. Dogs are very welcome. *Minimum stay: 2 nights at weekends. Children over 8 welcome.*

Rooms	18 doubles, 2 twins: £90-£250.
	1 suite for 2: £150-£163.
	Dinner, B&B, from £100 p.p.
Meals	Lunch from £8.50. À la carte dinner
	around £35.
Closed	Rarely.

David & Ruth Watson
The Crown & Castle
Orford, Woodbridge, IP12 2LJ
Tel   +44 (0)1394 450205
Email   info@crownandcastle.co.uk
Web   www.crownandcastle.co.uk

The Crown at Woodbridge

This cute little hotel in the middle of Woodbridge slopes downhill to the river, its palette of pastel colours making it a landmark in town. Inside, open-plan interiors flood with light courtesy of a glass ceiling. A Windermere skiff hangs above the bar, you find painted panelling, comfy sofas, slate floors and a wood-burner to keep things cosy. An airy restaurant comes in pale olive with leather banquettes, wooden floors and contemporary art, a fine spot for some tasty local food, perhaps seared scallops with Suffolk chorizo, slow braised pork with glazed carrots, white chocolate and passion fruit cheese cake. Breakfast is just as good; expect poached fruits, flagons of juice, smoked kippers, the best sausages in Suffolk. Bedrooms above vary in size, but all have the same feel: off-white colours, duck-down duvets, padded headboards, Hypnos beds. You'll find panels of entwined willow, pitchforks hanging on the wall, robes and power showers in sparkling bathrooms. Don't miss Sutton Hoo, the Aldeburgh food festival or Rendlesham Forest, the UK's equivalent of Area 51. *Minimum stay: 2 nights at weekends*

Rooms	8 twin/doubles: £110–£180.
	2 family rooms for 4: £140–£200.
	Extra beds/sofabeds £25 p.p.
Meals	Lunch & dinner £6–£30.
	Sunday lunch from £12.50.
Closed	Never.

Juliet Stone
The Crown at Woodbridge
Thoroughfare,
Woodbridge, IP12 1AD

Tel	+44 (0)1394 384242
Email	info@thecrownatwoodbridge.co.uk
Web	www.thecrownatwoodbridge.co.uk

Kesgrave Hall

This Georgian mansion sits in 38 acres of woodland and gardens, sound-proofing it from the outside world. It was home to US airmen during WWII, but the locals have reclaimed it as their own now and they come for the easy style, the excellent service, the delicious food and the informal vibe. The emphasis here is firmly on the food, so it's almost a restaurant with rooms, albeit quite a grand one. Inside, you find wellington boots in the entrance hall, high ceilings in the big sitting room, stripped boards in the humming bistro and doors that open onto a terrace in summer. Colourful bedrooms have lots of style. One is huge and comes with a free-standing bath and a faux leopard-skin sofa. The others might not be quite as wild, but they're lovely nonetheless, some cosy in the eaves, others in beautifully refurbished outbuildings. Expect warm colours, crisp linen, good lighting and fancy bathrooms. Back downstairs, tasty food flies from the kitchen, perhaps smoked haddock fishcakes, a char-grilled steak, a delicious coffee cheesecake with Tia Maria ice cream. Suffolk's magical coast waits.

Rooms	10 doubles, 7 twin/doubles: £130–£230. 6 suites for 2: £275–£300.
Meals	Breakfast £10–£16. Lunch & dinner, 3 courses, £25–£30.
Closed	Never.

Oliver Richards
Kesgrave Hall
Hall Road, Kesgrave,
Ipswich, IP5 2PU

Tel	+44 (0)1473 333741
Email	reception@kesgravehall.com
Web	www.milsomhotels.com

The Crown

The Crown is all things to all men, a lovely country pub, a popular local restaurant, a small boutique hotel, a welcoming bolthole in Constable country. It sits in a pretty village with long views from its colourful terrace over the Box Valley, not a bad spot for a glass of Pimm's after a day exploring the area. It dates to 1560 and has old beams and timber frames, though interiors have youthful good looks: warm colours, tongue-and-groove panelling, terracotta-tiled floors, a fancy wine cellar behind a wall of glass. You'll find rugs and settles, the daily papers, leather armchairs in front of a wood-burner. Four ales wait at the bar, 30 wines come by the glass and there's seasonal food that will make you smile, perhaps confit duck leg ravioli, pan-roasted cod with chorizo and crayfish, popcorn panna cotta. Airy bedrooms are quietly hidden away at the bottom of the garden — excellent beds, lovely linen, a dash of colour and super bathrooms. All have armchairs or sofas, three have French windows that open onto private terraces with fine views. A great place to eat, sleep and potter.

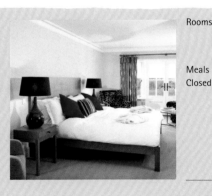

Rooms	10 doubles: £145-£250.
	1 suite for 2: £225-£295.
	Singles from £110. Extra bed/sofabed £20-£30 per person per night.
Meals	Lunch & dinner £5-£30.
Closed	25-26 December.

Richard Sunderland
The Crown
Park Street, Stoke-by-Nayland,
Colchester, CO6 4SE

Tel	+44 (0)1206 262001
Email	info@crowninn.net
Web	www.crowninn.net

The Bildeston Crown

Chris and Haley ran the Crown for ten years, upped sticks to head a few miles north, then got an offer they couldn't refuse and now the place is theirs. Their home is this beautifully preserved 15th-century inn. All the lovely old bits survive – timber frames, sagging beams, an ancient inglenook with a roaring fire – but interiors have an elegant, contemporary style with bold colours, stripped floorboards, comfy sofas and big art on the walls. Farmers drop in to chew the cud, walkers come to defrost in front of the fire while knocking back a pint of local ale, and the world and his wife come from near and far for Chris' delicious local food, perhaps truffled arancini with English asparagus, pheasant and foie gras Wellington, then an After Eight soufflé with chocolate ice cream. Stylish rooms have comfy beds, wonky floors, lots of colour and art. One has a fake Canaletto hanging above a claw-foot bath, another has a four-poster bed, all have robes in good bathrooms and flat-screen TVs. Don't miss Bury St Edmunds, a market town steeped in history. Medieval Lavenham is close, too. *Minimum stay: 2 nights at weekends.*

Rooms	11 doubles, 1 twin: £100–£175. Dinner, B&B from £87.50 p.p. Singles from £70.
Meals	Lunch from £6.50. Bar meals from £14. Dinner, 3 course, £30–£40. Sunday lunch from £17. Afternoon tea £15.
Closed	Never.

Hayley & Chris Lee
The Bildeston Crown
104 High Street,
Bildeston, IP7 7EB

Tel	+44 (0)1449 740510
Email	reception@thebildestoncrown.com
Web	www.thebildestoncrown.com

The Great House

The ingredients here are simple. Take a medieval wool town trapped in aspic, add a 15th-century merchant's house that overlooks the square, then whisk up the best food in Suffolk and you have one of the loveliest restaurants with rooms in the land. It sits opposite the Guildhall, its Georgian façade giving way to original interiors, where timber frames and old beams mix beautifully with light colours and varnished wood floors. A Suffolk institution for 30 years, it is French to its core, with a cheese board to beat all others. You eat in the airy dining room with an ancient fireplace in one corner, perhaps crab and prawn ravioli with lobster bisque foam followed by guinea fowl roulade with black tiger prawn mousse, then grapefruit and champagne Baba with marjoram cream. Bedrooms are just as good: timber frames, wonky floors, beautiful beds, a sofa is there's room. You'll find decanters of sherry, coffee machines, flat-screen TVs, robes in chic bathrooms. Four are huge, one has a regal four-poster, another a 14th-century fireplace in its bathroom. There's a courtyard for breakfast in the sun, too. *Minimum stay: 2 nights at weekends.*

Rooms	4 doubles, 1 twin/double: £105–£239. Singles from £105. Dinner, B&B from £119 per person. Extra bed/sofabed £15–£20 per person per night.
Meals	Breakfast £12–£17. Lunch £25 (not Mon/Tue). Dinner £36.50 (not Sun/Mon). Saturday night, à la carte only.
Closed	January; 2 weeks in October.

Thierry Pennec
The Great House
Market Place, Lavenham, CO10 9QZ

Tel	+44 (0)1787 247431
Email	info@greathouse.co.uk
Web	www.greathouse.co.uk

The Black Lion

This elegant inn is a valued part of Long Melford life, with locals propping up the bar and families booked in for Sunday lunch in the popular restaurant. Whether you're honeymooners or a holidaying clan, there's a bedroom to suit you (ten to choose from), and the Black Lion team look after you very well. You can even bring your well-behaved dog. Foodies will be in their element: local produce is the star here, from full Suffolk breakfasts, light lunches and pub classics to afternoon teas and a la carte dinners. Gin, beers and wines are often locally sourced too. Take over the conservatory if you come with a group. A five-minute walk into the village reveals a main street lined with cafes, restaurants and shops, with a definite emphasis on antiques and interiors. Cult TV series *Lovejoy* was filmed in the area for good reason. The Tudor splendour of Melford Hall, just a hundred yards away, is open to the public most days and hosts regular Elizabethan pageants.

Rooms	7 doubles: £89–£145.
	1 suite for 2: £165–£195.
	2 family rooms for 4: £99–£175.
Meals	Lunch from £8. Dinner from £14.
	Sunday lunch, 2 courses, £20.
Closed	Never.

Chris Poole
The Black Lion
The Green, Long Melford, CO10 9DN
Tel   +44 (0)1328 820235.
Email   info@theblacklionhotel.com
Web   www.theblacklionhotel.com

The Northgate

What do you want when you sneak off for a couple of days away? A small city steeped in history, beautiful country waiting beyond, a welcoming hotel with attractive bedrooms and excellent food? The Northgate – recently renovated from top to toe – offers all that and more. It's small and sits 500 metres from Abbey Gardens, the crown jewel of medieval Bury St Edmunds. Inside, the welcome is as warm as the water that pours from your power shower. Downstairs, the cocktail bar doubles as a sitting room, doors open onto a terrace for lunch in the sun, a well-kept garden waits beyond. Bedrooms above have a contemporary country-house feel: cool colours, smart wood furniture, pretty throws on beds that come with cool bedheads. Bathrooms are just as good: some have walk-in showers, two have freestanding baths in the room, all are excellent. As for the food, it's on tap all day: breakfast, elevenses, lunch, afternoon tea, then a delicious dinner, perhaps mackerel with apple and parsnip, rump of mutton with water chestnuts, an irresistible banana soufflé. Cambridge and Newmarket are close.

Rooms	7 doubles, 1 twin/double: £155-£225. 1 family room for 4: £280. Extra beds £15 p.p. per night.
Meals	Lunch from £6. Dinner, 3 courses, about £35; 9-course tasting menu £75.
Closed	Never.

Steve Smith
The Northgate
13-14 Northgate Street,
Bury St Edmunds, IP33 1HP
Tel   +44 (0)1284 339604
Email   info@thenorthgate.com
Web   www.thenorthgate.com

The Packhorse Inn

The rise of the cool country inn continues apace and the Packhorse is a prime example, a beautifully renovated country pub rescued from neglect. It's a small-scale pleasure dome – stylish interiors, ambrosial food, beautiful bedrooms and bathrooms – yet it remains a village local with a bar that welcomes all. The downstairs is open plan with a fire that burns on both sides and the odd armchair to take the strain. You'll find varnished floorboards, lots of art, lamps hanging above a cool bar. Chic bedrooms are scattered about. Coach house rooms have a warm rustic elegance, those in the house are a little fancier, a couple with baths in the room; all have fantastic bathrooms. Irresistible food waits below, maybe truffled goat's cheese with quince and figs, Suffolk venison and kidney pudding, plum tarte tatin with fruit-cake ice-cream. There's a terrace for good weather, then a private dining room that can turn into a meeting room. This is prime horse-racing country: Newmarket is three miles west, the peerless Frankel is at stud nearby. Cambridge and Bury St Edmunds are close.

Rooms	6 doubles, 2 twin/doubles: £100-£175. Singles from £85. Extra beds for children £10.
Meals	Lunch from £6. Dinner, 3 courses, about £35.
Closed	Rarely.

Michael Box
The Packhorse Inn
Bridge Street, Moulton,
Newmarket, CB8 8SP

Tel	+44 (0)1638 751818
Email	info@thepackhorseinn.com
Web	www.thepackhorseinn.com

Hurtwood Hotel

Wake to a full English breakfast; end the day with Tuscan tagiolini in the Italian-owned inn next door. Foodies beat a path to this sleepy village hotel, which was built in the 'roaring' Twenties by Trust House Forte in expectation of a railway line that never came. (Hence the peace.) Surrounded by forest walks and rolling pastures, you're in the heart of the village yet only an hour from London. Upstairs, spacious bedrooms have much comfort – those at the front are flooded with light, with views over the village to the hills. The friendliness is second to none, as are the little details, from the fresh milk in the fridge to the capsule coffee machine by your bed. There's a cycle shop opposite so hire a bike and follow a marked trail, or clamber up the hills of Box, Ranmore, and Leith (the second highest point in the south east of England). Or visit Polesden Lacey, a gracious house and garden with downland views. This area remains inexplicably undiscovered. *Pets by arrangement.*

Rooms	10 doubles, 3 twin/doubles: £85–£120. Extra beds: children £10; adults £15.
Meals	Lunch from £5.50. Bar meals from £9.50. Dinner, 3 courses, £25–£35; tasting menu £31.50.
Closed	Never.

Caroline Darbishire
Hurtwood Hotel
Walking Bottom, Peaslake, GU5 9RR

Tel	+44 (0)1306 730514
Email	hurtwoodhotel@mail.com
Web	www.hurtwoodhotel.co.uk

Entry 173   Map 3

Halfway Bridge Inn

This lovely country inn has exactly what lots of us want: warm and stylish interiors, local ales waiting in the bar, delicious food that draws a crowd, peaceful bedrooms for a good night's sleep. It sits back from the A272, with Goodwood to the south, Petworth to the east, and the South Downs all around for great walks and bike rides. Inside, you find a cosy world of original wood floors, whitewashed walls, smouldering fires, low beamed ceilings. It's all very cute, small but perfectly formed, with snug rooms giving a Dickensian feel. It dates to the mid-1700s and while a 21st-century makeover brought colour and style in equal measure, Sam made sure the inn lost none of its original charm. The airy bar has an open fire and 25 wines by the glass, then board games, the daily papers and doors onto a terrace for lunch in the sun. Big bedrooms in a stone barn wait across the lane. Expect sleigh beds, good bathrooms, beams and panelled walls. As for the food, it's a cut above, perhaps devilled kidneys, roasted guinea fowl, lemon and lavender terrine. Chichester and Arundel Castle are both close. *Minimum stay: 2 nights at weekends.*

Rooms	6 doubles: £145–£190. 1 suite for 2: £210–£230. Singles £90–£155. Extra bed/sofabed £30 per person per night.
Meals	Lunch from £6.50. Dinner, 3 courses, about £30. Sunday lunch from £16.50.
Closed	Never.

Sam Bakose
Halfway Bridge Inn
Halfway Bridge, Petworth, GU28 9BP

Tel	+44 (0)1798 861281
Email	enquiries@halfwaybridge.co.uk
Web	www.halfwaybridge.co.uk

Park House Hotel & Spa

This splendid country-house hotel sits in 10 acres of English gardens with quilted fields circling the grounds and the South Downs Way passing within a mile. Potter about outside and find a croquet lawn, two grass tennis courts and a six-hole golf course that slips into the country. Shrubberies burst with colour, there's a terrace for afternoon tea, wellington boots wait at the front door for long country walks. There's a beautiful spa, too. You can snooze on sunbeds while listening to birdsong on the terrace by the outdoor pool, or nip inside to the indoor pool and find treatment rooms, a sauna and a gym. The hotel is just as good, its country-house interiors filled with colour and style. You'll find an honesty bar that overlooks the garden, a sitting room for the daily papers, a conservatory that opens onto a terrace for scrumptious breakfasts. Smart rooms have heavenly beds, chic bathrooms, big country views, perhaps a terrace. Delicious food is the final delight, perhaps crab and ginger risotto, duck with honey-glazed parsnips, mint chocolate soufflé with passion fruit sorbet. Exceptional. *Minimum stay: 2 nights at weekends.*

Rooms	6 doubles, 10 twin/doubles: £130–£370. 4 family rooms for 4: £240–£370. 1 cottage for 4: £250–£385.
Meals	Lunch from £23.95. Dinner from £30. Afternoon tea £19.95.
Closed	25-26 December.

Mark Yates
Park House Hotel & Spa
Bepton,
Midhurst, GU29 0JB

Tel	+44 (0)1730 819020
Email	reservations@parkhousehotel.com
Web	www.parkhousehotel.com

The Crab & Lobster

This 17th-century whitewashed inn sits on Pangham Harbour, a tidal estuary that teems with preening birds. It's a peaceful stop, protected by a country lane mostly ignored by tourists. Inside, the restaurant/bar comes with a smouldering fire at one end and a wood-burner at the other. You'll find pretty art, fresh flowers and a chic alcove with banquette seating; in summer, life spills onto a terrace for lunch in the sun. Beautiful bedrooms come in duck-egg blue with crisp white linen, garden flowers, flat-screen TVs and chic bathrooms. Three have views across fields to the water, the other has a telescope with which to scan the high seas; the cottage has a well-equipped kitchen and a sitting room, too. By day you explore an area overflowing with history: Fishbourne Roman Palace; 11th-century Arundel Castle, and Bosham, where King Canute tried to turn back the waves;. Excellent food waits your return, perhaps Selsey crab and tiger prawn cocktail, filet of pork with burnt apple purée, peach tarte tatin with vanilla ice cream. The Witterings, for miles of beach and dunes, will help you walk it off. *Minimum stay: 2 nights at weekends.*

Rooms	4 doubles: £185–£215. 1 cottage for 4: £360–£370. Singles £100–£120. Extra bed/sofabed £30 p.p. per night.
Meals	Bar meals from £6.50. Lunch from £11.95. Dinner, 3 courses, £35. Sunday lunch, 2 courses, £26.
Closed	Never.

Sam Bakose
The Crab & Lobster
Mill Lane, Sidlesham,
Chichester, PO20 7NB

Tel   +44 (0)1243 641233
Email   enquiries@crab-lobster.co.uk
Web   www.crab-lobster.co.uk

The Bull

This 16th-century inn on the South Downs has won awards and with good reason – a cracking bar, beautiful bedrooms, tasty local food and an excellent array of ales and craft beers. Step inside where all is freshly and carefully made-over with extra space to dine among the many happy locals who gather for a pint of Bedlam, the pub's own brew. From the spanking new kitchen: menus using meat from Sussex farms, game from local estates, fish from short-range boats – try hay-smoked venison haunch with chervil root, chanterelles and kale, followed by rhubarb and citrus cheesecake with brown butter and Muscat. After dark, the big garden glows with light, fire pits are lit and blankets offered. Upstairs are stylish bedrooms with bags of character. Expect Farrow & Ball colours, chic fabrics, old-style radiators and comfy beds. Bigger rooms have sofas, all have digital radios, flat-screen TVs, rain showers in sparkling bathrooms, and freshly-baked cookies. Bring walking boots and mountain bikes, and scale the Ditchling Beacon for big views. Brighton and Gatwick are close. Don't miss Sunday lunch. *Minimum stay: 2 nights at weekends.*

Rooms	3 doubles, 1 twin/double: £100–£180.
Meals	Lunch & dinner from £12.
	Dinner, 3 courses, £25–£35.
	Sunday lunch from £15.
Closed	Never.

Dominic Worrall
The Bull
2 High Street, Ditchling, BN6 8TA

Tel	+44 (0)1273 843147
Email	info@thebullditchling.com
Web	www.thebullditchling.com

The Griffin Inn

It's not often you end up discussing the death of Athenian democracy with a barman, but that sort of thing is quite common here. The Griffin is English to its core, a posh inn with a streak of scruffiness, a community local that draws a devoted crowd. They come for the lively bar, the attractive restaurant and the club room for racing on Saturdays. In summer, life spills onto a smart terrace for local food cooked in a wood-fired oven. There's a bar in the garden, weekend barbecues, deckchairs scattered across the lawns for ten-mile views over Pooh Bear's Ashdown forest to Sheffield Park. Quirky bedrooms are nicely-priced. Some have wonky floors, others a four-poster, you'll find timber frames, lovely old furniture, then robes and free-standing baths; those in the coach house are quieter. Seasonal menus offer tasty rustic food, perhaps rabbit gnocchi, local pheasant, dark chocolate tort with honey ice cream; excellent wines help you wash it all down. The pub has three cricket teams that travel the world in pursuit of glory – you may find them in the bar on a summer evening after a hot day in the field. *Minimum stay: 2 nights bank holiday weekends.*

Rooms	6 doubles, 7 four-posters: £85–£150. Singles £70–£80 (Sun–Thur).
Meals	Bar meals from £6.50. Dinner, 3 courses, £30–£40.
Closed	Christmas Day.

Nigel & James Pullan
The Griffin Inn
Fletching, Uckfield, TN22 3SS

Tel	+44 (0)1825 722890
Email	info@thegriffininn.co.uk
Web	www.thegriffininn.co.uk

Wingrove House

This beautiful hotel is proof positive that small hotels are infinitely lovelier than their big brothers. It stands at the end of a pretty village with an ancient church on one side and the South Downs Way passing on the other. You enter through a walled garden that leads up to a stone terrace, where wisteria hangs from the balcony and bamboo sways in the breeze, a lovely spot to linger in good weather. In winter you retreat to the sitting room, where wood floors, an open fire and painted panelling give a warm contemporary feel. Super bedrooms have cool colours, smart fabrics and robes in excellent bathrooms. Two open onto the veranda, the biggest at the back overlooks the churchyard, some have double-ended baths, others vast walk-in showers. The restaurant, recently refurbished, has a chic rustic feel. An open fire keeps things cosy on colder nights, a wall of glass opens onto a dining terrace in summer. Delicious food waits, perhaps locally smoked salmon, slow-braised venison, sticky toffee pudding with slated caramel ice cream. Walks start from the front door: Cuckmere Haven and Beachy Head wait.

Rooms	12 doubles: £100–£195.
	1 cottage for 5: £750–£1200 per week.
Meals	Light lunch from £4.50 (Mon–Sat).
	Dinner, 2–3 courses, £29–£35.
	Sunday lunch, 2–3 courses, £25–£29.
Closed	Never.

Simon Corbett
Wingrove House
High Street, Alfriston,
Polegate, BN26 5TD

Tel   +44 (0)1323 870276
Email   info@wingrovehousealfriston.com
Web   www.wingrovehousealfriston.com

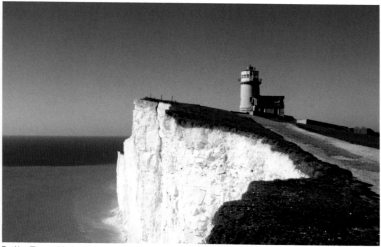

Belle Tout Lighthouse

A fine old lighthouse atop a white cliff with stunning views in every direction. To your left, Beachy Head, to your right, Birling Gap – it's a magical position with the South Downs rolling down into the English Channel. As for the lighthouse, it dates to 1832. It was once moved 57 feet back to stop it crumbling into the sea and it featured prominently in the BBC's production of *The Life and Loves of a She-Devil*. It re-opened in 2010 after a splendid renovation as a lovely little B&B hotel. Bedrooms are rather wonderful: not huge, but all have windows that bring the outside in. You get white walls to soak up the light, fantastic views of rolling hills, pretty fabrics, lovely linen, the odd exposed brick wall; shower rooms are small but sweet, one room has a bath. Ian's legendary breakfasts are served on high with views of sea and cliff. There's a wood-burner in the sitting room, where guests gather each night before climbing up to explore the lantern. Good food waits in the village: a lovely pub and an excellent Thai restaurant. Magnificent walking waits. *Minimum stay: 2 nights. Over 15s welcome.*

Rooms	6 doubles: £160-£240.
	Singles £108-£204.
Meals	Pub/restaurant within 1 mile.
Closed	Christmas & New Year.

Ian Noall
Belle Tout Lighthouse
Beachy Head Road, Beachy Head,
Eastbourne, BN20 0AE

Tel	+44 (0)1323 423185
Email	info@belletout.co.uk
Web	www.belletout.co.uk

Strand House

As you follow the Royal Military Canal down to miles of sandy beach, bear in mind that 600 years ago, you'd have been swimming in the sea. This is reclaimed land and Strand House, built in 1425, originally stood on Winchelsea Harbour. Outside, you find wandering wisteria, colourful flowerbeds and a woodland walk that leads up to the village. Inside, medieval interiors have low ceilings, timber frames and mind-your-head beams. There are reds and yellows, sofas galore, a wood-burner in the sitting room, an honesty bar from which to help yourself. It's a home-spun affair: Hugh cooks breakfast, Mary looks after guests in style. Quirky bedrooms sweep you back in time. One has an ancient four-poster, some have wonky floors, three open onto a terrace, all have good beds and robes for tiny shower rooms. As for the cottage, airy rooms have more space, and the suite, with its balcony and views, is a treat. The house, once a work house, was painted by Turner and Millais. Local restaurants wait: Webbe's at The Fish Café, The Kings Head in Rye, top notch food at the Curlew in Bodiam. *Minimum stay: 2 nights at weekends & in high season. 3 dog-friendly rooms available.*

Rooms	5 doubles, 1 twin/double, 5 triples; 1 double with separate bath: £80–£150. 1 suite for 4: £180. Singles from £60. Extra beds £25 per person. Dogs £7.50.
Meals	Dinner for groups by arrangements (minimum 8 people)
Closed	Rarely.

Mary Sullivan & Hugh Davie
Strand House
Tanyards Lane, Winchelsea,
Rye, TN36 4JT

Tel	+44 (0)1797 226276
Email	info@thestrandhouse.co.uk
Web	www.thestrandhouse.co.uk

The George in Rye

Rye is beautiful, old England trapped in aspic. It was a Cinque Port, Henry James lived here and the oldest church clock in England chimes at the top of the hill. The George stands on its cobbled High Street right in the thick of things. Built in 1575 from reclaimed ships' timbers, its exposed beams and panelled walls remain on display. Inside, old and new mix beautifully – expect Jane Austen in the 21st century. There's a roaring fire in the bar, screen prints of the Beatles on the walls in reception, a sun-trapping courtyard for lunch in summer. Beautiful bedrooms come in all shapes and sizes (a couple are small), but chic fabrics, Frette linen and Vi-Spring mattresses are standard, as are good books, fine bathrooms, white robes and cashmere covers on hot water bottles. Some are huge with zinc baths in the room, one has a round bed. You eat in the George Grill, an open kitchen on display, perhaps Provençal fish soup, grilled rib-eye with hand-cut chips, gooseberry soufflé with bay leaf ice cream. Walk it off by following the river down to the sea. *Mapp and Lucia* was filmed in the town.

Rooms	8 doubles, 21 twin/doubles: £135–£195.
	5 suites for 2: £295–£325.
	Singles from £95.
Meals	Lunch from £6.
	Dinner, 3 courses, £30–£40.
	Afternoon tea £12.50.
Closed	Never.

Alex & Katie Clarke
The George in Rye
98 High Street,
Rye, TN31 7JT

Tel	+44 (0)1797 222114
Email	alex@thegeorgeinrye.com
Web	www.thegeorgeinrye.com

Jeake's House

Rye is gorgeous, one of those lovely English towns that's been around for centuries, but has never lost its looks. The same is true of Jeake's House, which sits in the old town on a pretty cobbled street away from the crowds. In its 300-year history it's been a wool store, a school and the home of American poet Conrad Potter Aiken. Inside, style abounds. The galleried dining room – once an old Baptist chapel – is now painted deep red and full of busts, books, clocks and mirrors, a fine setting for your bacon and eggs. There's a raffish bar, where a fire burns in winter, then a pretty sitting room with a Broadwood square piano. Potter about and find timber frames, ancient beams and some strikingly furnished bedrooms; several have four-posters, one has a telly concealed in the wood-burner, all are deeply comfortable and excellent value for money. As for Rye, art galleries, antiques shops, old churches and river walks wait; don't miss the Summer Exhibition in early September. All this would be blossom in the wind without Jenny, whose natural joie de vivre makes this a very special place. *Children over 8 welcome.*

Rooms	7 twin/doubles; 1 double with separate bath: £95–£128. 3 suites for 2: £130–£150.
Meals	Restaurants within walking distance.
Closed	Never.

Jenny Hadfield
Jeake's House
Mermaid Street,
Rye, TN31 7ET

Tel	+44 (0)1797 222828
Email	stay@jeakeshouse.com
Web	www.jeakeshouse.com

Entry 183   Map 4

The Gallivant

This cool little hotel stands across the road from Camber Sands, where five miles of pristine beach are home to kite surfers, beach cricketers and sun worshipers alike. As for the Gallivant, a recent refurbishment has brought a stunning new look to every corner. Bedrooms, small and large, and now things of great beauty. Snug cabin rooms are clad in wood with brass lamps hanging from the ceiling; baby Hamptons have daybeds and marble bathrooms; deck rooms at the back come in cool whites with doors onto private terraces. Then come the garden rooms – heaven for hedonists – with double-ended baths in the room (and doors that slide for privacy), then small decks in the garden, where you'll also find a massage hut and deckchairs in summer. All have great storage, flawless bathrooms and crisp linen for Hypnos beds. As for the food, most is sourced within 10 miles and you eat in an airy restaurant that opens onto a terrace in summer, perhaps cod with lime and cucumber, salt marsh lamb with root veg, chocolate torte with Frangelico jelly. There's tea and cake 'on the house' every afternoon, too. *Minimum stay: 2 nights at weekends. Pets by arrangement.*

Rooms	20 doubles, some with garden access and terraces: £95–£245. Singles £85–£240.
Meals	Lunch from £16. Dinner, 3 courses, from £35.
Closed	Rarely.

Elise Roberts
The Gallivant
New Lydd Road,
Camber, Rye, TN31 7RB

Tel	+44 (0)1797 225057
Email	enquiries@thegallivant.co.uk
Web	www.thegallivant.co.uk

The Bell Alderminster

A lively inn on the Alscot estate with gardens that run down to a small river. There's a beautiful terrace, too, a popular spot for lunch in the sun, washed down by a pint of home-brewed ale. Inside, chic interiors mix of old and new to great effect – low beamed ceilings and exposed brick walls, then lots of colour and leather banquettes. You'll find candles everywhere, armchairs in front of the fire, black-and-white screen prints of estate life. Recent additions include an airy new restaurant with a wall of glass that opens onto the terrace, then a balcony above, where you can scoff afternoon tea while gazing out on open country. There's good food, too, with lamb and beef straight from the estate. You'll find sharing plates, soups and salads, perhaps seared tuna with chilli fritters, rump steak with a pepper sauce, banana sponge with toffee ice cream. Stylish bedrooms have smart fabrics, crisp linen, sofas or armchairs if there's room. Two are small, the suites are enormous and have gorgeous bathrooms. A road passes to the front, quietly at night. Stratford waits up the road for all things Shakespeare.

Rooms	5 doubles, 2 twins: £100–£145. 2 suites for 2: £150–£170. Singles from £70 (Sun-Thur).
Meals	Bar meals from £7. Lunch, 2 courses from £14.50. Dinner, 3 courses from £18. Sunday lunch, 3 courses, £25.
Closed	Never.

Sean Piernan
The Bell Alderminster
Shipston Road, Alderminster,
Stratford-upon-Avon, CV37 8NY
Tel   +44 (0)1789 450414
Email   info@thebellald.co.uk
Web   www.thebellald.co.uk

The Howard Arms

The Howard stands on Ilmington Green, eight miles south of Stratford-upon-Avon. It was built at roughly the same time as Shakespeare wrote *King Lear* and little has changed since. It's a lovely country inn and comes with original fixtures and fittings: polished flagstones, heavy beams, mellow stone walls, a crackling fire. Outside, roses ramble on golden stone walls, while a pretty garden waits at the back. Good food comes as standard, perhaps ham hock terrine with homemade piccalilli, marinated duck breast with bok choy, apple tarte tatin with mascarpone cream; there's fish and chips and a good burger, too. Elsewhere, you find oils on walls, books on shelves, settles in alcoves, beautiful bay windows. A colourful dining room floods with light courtesy of fine arched windows that overlook the green. Bedrooms in the main house have a charming old-world feel, garden rooms are more contemporary with excellent bathrooms. You can walk across fields to Chipping Campden; Simon de Montfort once owned this land. The village church dates to the 11th century and has Thompson mice within.

Rooms	5 doubles, 3 twin/doubles: £110-£150. Singles £88-£120. Extra bed/sofabed £25 per person per night.
Meals	Lunch from £4.50. Bar meals from £9.50. Dinner, 3 courses, £25-£30.
Closed	Never.

Robert Jeal
The Howard Arms
Lower Green,
Ilmington, CV36 4LT

Tel	+44 (0)1608 682226
Email	info@howardarms.com
Web	www.howardarms.com

The Rectory Hotel

This Georgian rectory dates to 1780 and sits in two acres of English gardens, with the church tower peeping up above fine tress. From the outside, little has changed in a hundred years, but step inside and find a newly refurbished house that sparkles at every turn. There's a chic sitting with a roaring fire and beautiful art, then a restaurant that starts in a panelled dining room and flows into a conservatory, where doors open onto the garden for breakfast on the lawn in summer. Rooms above are just as good – super beds, stylish fabrics, perhaps a claw-foot bath in your room or ceilings open to the rafters. Light floods in, bigger rooms have sofas, all have contemporary elegance in spades. You get smart TVs (and movies to stream), super-fast WiFi, then robes in magical bathrooms. Back downstairs, a chic bar opens onto the garden for Pimm's in the sun; keep going and find sunbeds circling the swimming pool. Glorious food rounds off your day, perhaps Cornish scallops, roast veal, Florentine doughnuts with Chantilly cream. Don't miss the occasional festival at their sister pub across the road.

Rooms	15 doubles: £150–£230.
	Child bed available £25.
Meals	Lunch from £6.50. Dinner, 3 courses, about £35. Sunday lunch from £18.
Closed	Never.

	Alex Payne
	The Rectory Hotel
	Crudwell, Malmesbury, SN16 9EP
Tel	+44 (0)1666 577194
Email	alex@romanroadproperties.com
Web	www.therectoryhotel.com

The Methuen Arms

The Methuen has changed with the times. It started life as a 14th-century nunnery, turned into a coaching inn in 1608, then had a Georgian facelift in the late 1700s. In 2010 it was reborn as a chic boutique hotel – cosy and stylish with great food and delicious Butcombe ales. It sits on the edge of the village, with an avenue of trees around the corner that lead up to Corsham Court, an Elizabethan pile. As for the hotel, there's a sun-trapping courtyard where you can eat in summer, a restaurant that opens onto the garden, a locals' bar where the main currency is gossip, then a sitting-room bar where you can sink into an armchair in front of the wood-burner. It's all very pretty, an easy style runs throughout. You'll find shuttered windows, the odd beam, the daily papers, rugs on wood floors. Gorgeous bedrooms have warm colours, padded bedheads, good art, Roberts radios. There are robes in fine bathrooms, four of which have claw-foot baths, one of which is in the bedroom. Super food waits, perhaps cream of shallot soup, venison with heritage carrots, Wiltshire honey crème caramel. Bath is close.

Rooms	11 doubles, 2 twin/doubles: £140-£175. 1 family room for 4: £150-£220. Singles from £90.
Meals	Lunch from £5.95. Dinner, 3 courses, about £30. Sunday lunch from £18.50.
Closed	Never.

Ashley Harlow & Abigail Vince
The Methuen Arms
2 High Street, Corsham, SN13 0HB

Tel	+44 (0)1249 717060
Email	info@themethuenarms.com
Web	www.themethuenarms.com

Timbrell's Yard

Those lovely people at the Stay Original Company have been doing what they do so well – opening another of their small-scale pleasuredomes. Timbrell's Yard stands close to the bridge in Bradford-on-Avon with beautiful views across the river to the churchyard. Outside, a terrace at the front catches the sun, with this 18th-century listed building standing grandly behind. It's a lovely spot, good enough for Samuel Spode to paint; a copy of his work hangs in the restaurant, the real thing waits in the town's museum. Inside, you get that winning combination of stylish rooms, lovely food and well-kept ales, with cakes and coffee available all day. You'll find stripped floors, hanging lamps, exposed stone walls, then sofas in front of an open fire. Helpful staff weave about, delivering food that makes you smile, perhaps Dorset crab on toast, pork belly with sea salt crackling, vanilla panna cotta with rhubarb jelly. Bedrooms are beautiful. Fourteen have river views, two have baths in the room, mezzanine suites have window seats where you can watch the river pass. Bathrooms are predictably divine.

Rooms	17 doubles: £85–£195.
	Extra beds for children £20.
Meals	Lunch & dinner £5–£35.
Closed	Never.

Henry Gray
Timbrell's Yard
49 St Margaret's Street,
Bradford-on-Avon, BA15 1DE

Tel	+44 (0)1225 869492
Email	info@timbrellsyard.com
Web	timbrellsyard.com

Widbrook Grange

Sink into the chesterfield by the fire and enjoy an outstanding G&T. With 125 craft gins on the menu and 14 tonics this is G&T Central. Not only that, the food is largely locally sourced with herbs from the garden and a sophisticated menu, and you can have your wedding party or special gathering here. We love this Georgian country-house hotel in 11 acres of grounds at the end of a track, close to Bath and Bradford-on-Avon. Choose from bedrooms in the house or over in the ground-floor stables. You'll find the staff a delight and their welcome extends to families and dogs: note the dog baskets and the rabbit-rich grounds. Stroll down to the canal and walk along the tow path, or hire a narrow boat for the day. Stay put and use the gym and indoor heated pool, book a massage and treatment, have afternoon tea.

Rooms	6 doubles: £105–£220. 8 twin/doubles: £125–£165. 1 suite for 2: £165–£220. 4 family rooms for 3: £145–£205.
Meals	Lunch from £13. Dinner, 3 courses, £35. Sunday lunch, 2 courses, £24.95. Afternoon tea from £8.95.
Closed	Never.

Hakan Tiryaki
Widbrook Grange
Bradford-on-Avon, BA15 1UH
Tel　　+44 (0)1225 864750
Email　stay@widbrookgrange.co.uk
Web　　www.widbrookgrange.co.uk

Entry 190　Map 3

The Lamb at Hindon

The Lamb has been serving ale on Hindon's high street for 800 years. It's a yard of England's finest cloth, a place where shooting parties come to eat and farmers meet to chew the cud. Inside you find oak settles, roaring fires and painted panelling. A clipped Georgian elegance lingers; you almost expect Mr Darcy to walk in, give a tormented sigh, then turn on his heels and vanish. You'll find flagstone floors, stripped boards, window seats and gilded mirrors, then a pine booth, where officials sat collecting tolls from passing travellers. At night, candles come out, as do some excellent wines, and you dig into lovely food: perhaps ham hock with piccalilli, roast quail with parsnips, bread and butter pudding. Refurbished rooms have pretty colours, crisp linen, smart bathrooms and Bakelite phones. Some even have their own private gardens. Expect padded headboards, lovely art, a huge lampshade or a claw-foot bath. Three suites in converted outhouses have an elegant contemporary style with vintage luggage, the odd chandelier and lovely bathrooms. Stourhead and Stonehenge are close. *Minimum stay: 2 nights at weekends May-September.*

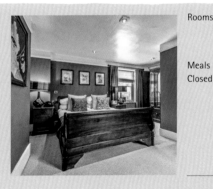

Rooms	9 doubles, 3 twins: £99–£149. 3 suites for 2: £129–£179. Extra bed/sofabed £15–£20 p.p. per night. Dogs £20.
Meals	Lunch & dinner £5–£35.
Closed	Never.

Bernice Gallagher
The Lamb at Hindon
High Street, Hindon,
Salisbury, SP3 6DP

Tel	+44 (0)1747 820573
Email	lambhindon@youngs.co.uk
Web	www.lambhindon.co.uk

The Beckford Arms

A country-house inn on the Fonthill estate. You sweep in under the Triumphal Arch, which seems appropriate – this is one of the loveliest inns in the land. Outside, in the garden, you find hammocks in the trees and parasols on the terrace, then a church spire soaring beyond. Georgian interiors are no less lovely, a mix of original features and 21st-century style. There's a drawing room with facing sofas in front of a roaring fire; a restaurant with a wall of glass that opens onto the terrace; a bar with parquet flooring for an excellent local pint. Potter about and chance upon the odd chandelier, roaming wisteria and a rather grand mahogany table in the private dining room. Bedrooms are small but perfectly formed with prices to match: white walls, the best linen, sisal matting, good bathrooms. If you want something bigger try the pavilions on the estate; former guests include Byron and Nelson, though we doubt they had it so good. As for the food, it's lovely stuff, perhaps Brixham clam chowder, whole lemon sole, chocolate and Cointreau delice with blood orange sorbet. One of the best.

Rooms	7 doubles, 1 twin/double: £95–£120.
	2 pavilions for 2: £175–£195.
Meals	Dinner about £30.
Closed	Christmas.

Charlie Luxton
The Beckford Arms
Fonthill Gifford, Tisbury,
Salisbury, SP3 6PX

Tel	+44 (0)1747 870385
Email	info@beckfordarms.com
Web	www.beckfordarms.com

Howard's House

This ancient village is a dream, a wormhole back in time, a fitting stage for this Grade-II listed house that dates to 1623. Outside, fine gardens sweep uphill to a ridge of old oak, where views stretch out across the valley. Inside, warm country-house interiors come with the odd beam, fine arched windows and original flagstones in the hall. You'll find smart sofas, fresh flowers and the morning papers in the cosy sitting room, where a fire crackles on colder days. In summer, doors open onto a pretty terrace, where you can breakfast in good weather. Elegant bedrooms are deeply comfortable with pretty fabrics, mullioned windows and super-comfy beds. You get bowls of fruit, a sofa if there's room, then robes in spotless bathrooms. Spin downstairs for some lovely country food, perhaps wood pigeon with garlic, lemon sole with crab bisque, passion fruit soufflé with mango sorbet; climb back up afterwards to find your bed turned down. Uplifting walks start from the front door, the renovated coach house is perfect for small parties. Salisbury, Stonehenge and the gardens at Stourhead are close.

Rooms	6 doubles, 2 twin/doubles, 1 four-poster: £190-£225. Singles from £120.
Meals	Lunch from £25. Dinner, seasonal menu £28-£33.50; à la carte £37-£46.50; 6-course tasting menu £80.
Closed	5 days over Christmas.

Simon Greenwood
Howard's House
Teffont Evias, Salisbury, SP3 5RJ

Tel	+44 (0)1722 716392
Email	enq@howardshousehotel.co.uk
Web	www.howardshousehotel.co.uk

Entry 193   Map 3

The Lygon Arms Hotel

This hotel has a guest book signed by Pierce Brosnan and Kylie Minogue but you, your children, and the dog will be welcomed with equal grace. There's much to do in a huge choice of drawing rooms and good food and drinks are served in several different areas, all lively and bustling. This isn't an old-fashioned hushed sort of place: staff wear a uniform but there's a light-hearted feel and they are über efficient without being in the least fawning. Children can go to Kids' Club, you can wind down in the spa and there's even a warm water tap for hosing down your dog. And across the road there are three acres to explore. Broadway has two museums, a fantastic deli and lots of independent – rather expensive – shops, but you're on holiday. Walk to Broadway Tower in half an hour, hop on a steam train or hire bikes. Return for drinks in the atmospheric cocktail bar before dinner. *Minimum stay: 2 nights at weekends. Parking on-site.*

Rooms	27 doubles, 31 twin/doubles: £225–£280. 26 suites for 4 with extra bed for child available: £360. Extra bed/sofabed £25–£65 p.p. per night.
Meals	Lunch from £9. Dinner from £15. Afternoon tea from £10.
Closed	Never.

Reservations
The Lygon Arms Hotel
High Street, Broadway, WR12 7DU
Tel   +44 (0)1386 852255
Email   reservations@lygonarmshotel.co.uk
Web   www.lygonarmshotel.co.uk

The Fish Hotel

Come for Scandi chic on a smart estate with some perfectly well-priced rooms. It's like summer camp, only for adults – a place designed for fun. Expect a striking simplicity with airy colours, white linen, padded bedheads, robes in sparkling bathrooms. Rooms are scattered about in pretty buildings on the hill, the suites altogether fancier with claw-foot baths in the room, huge beds, maybe a sofa or a wood-burner, too. They spiral around a central lodge, where you can eat, drink and be merry. If the style is coolly contemporary, then the feel is cosy and informal, with lovely staff on hand to help. The big bar is the hub: sofas galore, cool colours, walls of glass that open onto a terrace, a funky wood-burner for winter nights. There's a games room for pool and table football and 400 acres of countryside to explore from the door. Deer roam the hill, there's a nature trail and maps for joggers. As for the food, you can eat in the bar, the restaurant, or out on the terrace in good weather.

Rooms	10 doubles, 33 twin/doubles: £150-£255. 4 suites for 2: £230-£275.
Meals	Lunch from £5. Dinner, 3 courses, £25-£35.
Closed	Never.

Zena Carter
The Fish Hotel
Farncombe Estate,
Broadway, WR12 7LJ

Tel	+44 (0)1386 858000
Email	reservations@thefishhotel.co.uk
Web	www.thefishhotel.co.uk

Brocco on the Park

Sheffield is a friendly city, an arty hub that's full of surprises, a fact ably demonstrated by this stunning small hotel. It sits amid leafy streets, with a smart park to the front, then hills beyond that ripple over to the Peak District. Picasso stayed here when he attended the World Peace Conference in 1950, though things have changed a little since – a recent refit has turned this into a small-scale pleasure dome. Downstairs, there's a Scandi feel in the café/kitchen, with joggers and dog walkers swapping the park for delicious smoothies or a slice of cake. Bedrooms are divine, as good as they look. Expect the best white linen, smart neutral colours, the coolest bathrooms with robes and organic oils. A vast window in one room opens to frame the view; another has a free-standing bath; all are named after birds, their colours reflected in the fabrics. Back downstairs, tasty food waits at night, perhaps cauliflower and pistachio fritters, rib-eye steak with wild mushrooms, spiced plum crumble with vanilla ice cream. Don't miss the Millennium Gallery, the Winter Garden or the cool streets around you.

Rooms	6 doubles, 2 twin/doubles: £110–£240. Extra bed/sofabed £35 p.p. per night.
Meals	Breakfasts from £7. Lunch from £7. Dinner from £12. Sunday lunch from £16.
Closed	Rarely.

Tiina Carr
Brocco on the Park
92 Brocco Bank,
Sheffield, S11 8RS

Tel	+44 (0)114 266 1233
Email	hello@brocco.co.uk
Web	www.brocco.co.uk

Entry 196   Map 6

The Parisi Hotel

This lovely small hotel makes a great base for a night or two in glorious York. It stands within the Roman wall, opposite St Denys Church, which lost its spire to cannon fire in the Civil War. It's all the work of two sisters, Sophie and Maria, who renovated from top to toe, bringing a chic, colourful style to this Victorian rectory. Inside, you'll find original art on every wall in the airy breakfast room, sofas in front of the wood-burner in the beautiful library, then a door that leads out to a gravelled courtyard, where you can sink into wicker armchairs when the sun shines. Bedrooms are just as good: cool colours, smart fabrics, excellent beds, '60s retro furniture. You get lots of art, coffee machines, iPhone players, flat-screen TVs. Some rooms are smaller, all have sparkling bathrooms, one has a free-standing bath in the room. Cross the river, weave through lanes, arrive at York Minster, one of the largest Gothic cathedrals in Europe. Back at the hotel, five excellent restaurants wait within 200 metres. Northern Soul nights take place locally, too. You won't want to leave. *Minimum stay: 2 nights on weekends.*

Rooms	10 doubles: £99–£189.
	1 suite for 2: £179–£229.
Meals	Restaurants 2-minute walk.
Closed	Three weeks in January.

Maria & Sophie Scott
The Parisi Hotel
51 St Denys Road,
York, YO1 9QD

Tel	+44 (0)1904 658815
Email	info@theparisi.com
Web	www.theparisi.com

West Park Hotel

Harrogate made its name in Georgian England as a spa town for the gentry. These days it holds the title of 'happiest place to live in Britain.' It's also one of the prettiest, with grand houses, leafy streets and the Stray, 200 acres of park and gardens that unfurls itself directly opposite this stylish hotel. Outside, you can sit at tables and watch the world go by. Inside, the bar and restaurant come as one, a lively spot that draws a crowd and comes with leather booths, chic bar stools, lots of colour and style. Cocktails, locals ales, wines from around the world all wait, as does some excellent bistro food, perhaps moules marinière, rack of lamb, apple and caramel tart. Bedrooms are lovely: crisp linen, the best mattresses, smart TVs and cool bathrooms. Bigger rooms at the front overlook the Stray, smaller ones at the back share the same style. Stay on a Sunday night and you can 'eat your bill;' whatever you spend on dinner will be removed from the cost of your room! Don't miss the Turkish baths or the gardens at Harlow Carr.

Rooms	11 doubles, 6 twin/doubles: £125–£245. 6 suites for 2, 2 suites for 4: £205–£365. Singles from £110. Extra bed £10.
Meals	Breakfast from £3.95. Lunch from £6.50. Dinner, 3 courses, £25–£40. Afternoon tea from £12.95. Sunday lunch from £14.95.
Closed	Never.

Nathan George
West Park Hotel
19 West Park Road,
Harrogate, HG1 1BJ

Tel   +44 (0)1423 524471
Email   enquiries@thewestparkhotel.com
Web   thewestparkhotel.com

The Angel Inn

The old drovers' inn remains staunchly, reassuringly traditional – but offers wines that have come, over the years, to rival the hand-pumped Yorkshire ales. There's even a 'cave' for functions and private-party tastings. Expect nooks, crannies, beams and crackling fires, and a stylish restaurant. Thought has gone into every detail, from the antique furniture in the timbered rooms (one with a marvellous oak-panelled bar) to the fabrics and the colours. Menus change with each season and include dishes ranging from filo 'moneybags' of seafood in lobster sauce – the fish comes fresh from Fleetwood – to their own Yorkshire twist on tapas ('Yapas'!). Vegetarians are looked after and the sticky toffee pudding is legendary. Exquisite bedrooms, split between the converted barn and adjacent Sycamore House, are all different; perhaps a French armoire, a brass bed, a claw-foot bath, a private garden. All have top-quality fabrics, pretty colours, cosy bathrooms, and, in the newer rooms, a contemporary feel. The glorious up-hill-and-down-dale drive to get here is part of the charm.

Rooms	9 doubles: £150–£175.
	5 suites for 2: £175–£200.
	Singles from £125. Extra beds £25.
Meals	Lunch from £7.50. Bar meals from £15.95. Dinner, 3 courses, £35–£55. Sunday lunch £24.50.
Closed	Christmas Day & 1 week in January.

Juliet Watkins
The Angel Inn
Hetton, Skipton, BD23 6LT
Tel   +44 (0)1756 730263
Email   info@angelhetton.co.uk
Web   www.angelhetton.co.uk

The Traddock

A northern outpost of country-house charm, beautiful inside and out. It's a family affair and those looking for a friendly base from which to explore the Dales will find it here. You enter through the drawing room — crackling fire, pretty art, the daily papers, cavernous sofas. Potter about and find polished wood in the dining room, panelled walls in the breakfast room, then William Morris wallpaper in the sitting room bar, where you can sip a pint of Skipton ale while playing Scrabble. Bedrooms are gorgeous, some coolly contemporary, others warmly traditional. The star of the show is the new suite — sand-blasted timbers, a lovely big sofa, a stunning free-standing bath — but all are charming, with chic fabrics, warm colours, comfy beds and the odd claw-foot bath. Downstairs, a white-washed sitting room opens onto the garden for afternoon tea, while delicious food waits in the restaurant, perhaps seafood chowder, braised lamb shank, apple and calvados mousse. Walks start at the front door, there are cycle tracks, even caves to explore (one is bigger than St Paul's). Unbeatable. *Minimum stay: 2 nights at weekends March-November.*

Rooms	8 doubles, 1 twin/double: £95–£165. 2 suites for 2: £180–£235. 2 family rooms for 4: £95–£175. Dinner, B&B £85–£160 p.p. Extra bed/sofabed £25 p.p. per night.
Meals	Lunch from £9.50. Dinner, 3 courses, around £30. Picnics from £7.50. Afternoon tea from £15.95.
Closed	Never.

Paul Reynolds
The Traddock
Austwick, Settle, LA2 8BY

Tel	+44 (0)15242 51224
Email	info@thetraddock.co.uk
Web	www.thetraddock.co.uk

The White Bear Hotel

At five o'clock on Friday evenings there's only one place to be in Masham: the tap room of the White Bear, home of Theakston's beer. The great and the good gather to mark the end of the week, the odd pint is sunk, the air is thick with gossip. Interior design is 1920s trapped in aspic: red leather, polished brass, a crackling fire. But there's only half the story. Slip next door and discover this welcoming inn. There's an smart dining room, stripped boards in the bar, a flower-filled terrace for lunch in the sun. Stylish rooms occupy the old Lightfoot brewery and come in contemporary style, with warm colours, comfy beds, chic new bathrooms and attractive prices. Some have views across town, the penthouse is vast and open to the rafters. There's a courtyard for guests, a sitting room, too; staff will bring drinks if you want privacy and peace. Good food waits in the restaurant, perhaps king scallops, duck with red cabbage, treacle sponge pudding. Tours of the brewery are easily arranged, with a pint of your choice at the end. Don't miss the beer festival in June or the sheep fare in September.

Rooms	12 twin/doubles: £130-£125.
	1 suite for 2: £200.
	2 family rooms for 4: £130-£155.
	Dogs £15 per night. Extra bed
	available £15 per night.
Meals	Lunch from £5. Bar meals from £11.95.
	Dinner, 3 courses, about £30.
Closed	Never.

Sue Thomas
The White Bear Hotel
Wellgarth, Masham,
Ripon, HG4 4EN

Tel	+44 (0)1765 689319
Email	sue@whitebearmasham.co.uk
Web	www.thewhitebearhotel.co.uk

The Burgoyne Hotel

It's utterly peaceful here and you're looked after beautifully by Leigh and her team. You can set up camp in one of two drawing rooms that share an inglenook fireplace and there are books, games and magazines. Bring bikes or hire them from two minutes away (there's a lockable shed for when you get back) and head to the hills, pack a picnic and walk all day without meeting another soul, spot rare birds including lapwings, explore 14th-century Bolton Castle or historic Richmond. Stroll along the river or visit the craft shops in town, return to a big tea of sandwiches and scones with cream or save yourself for pre-dinner drinks and canapés then à la carte or the full tasting menu in the restaurant.

Rooms	6 doubles, 2 twin/doubles; 2 doubles, 1 twin, all with private bathrooms: £99–£235. Singles from £81.50. Extra beds for children under 13: £25.
Meals	Dinner, 2 courses, £28; 3 courses, £34. Tasting menu £42.
Closed	3–31 January.

Leigh O'Donoghue
The Burgoyne Hotel
Reeth, Richmond,
Swaledale, DL11 6SN

Tel	+44 (0)1748 884292
Email	enquiries@theburgoyne.co.uk
Web	www.theburgoyne.co.uk

The Coach House at Middleton Lodge

You'll think you've washed up in Tuscany or Provence. These gorgeous stone barns were crumbling a few years ago, now they're home to one of the loveliest hotels in the north. In summer, life spills onto the courtyard for lunch in the sun, but step through the arched glass doors and find a spectacular restaurant open to the rafters, where contemporary design mixes with rustic bricks and mortar. There's a funky bar, an open fire, a sitting room for guests that opens onto a terrace. Rooms are just as good, with chic fabrics, Roberts radios, super-comfy beds and robes in cool bathrooms. Five open onto a terrace, most have claw-foot baths. Elsewhere, you'll find a couple of treatment rooms, a two-acre kitchen garden where you can get married, and six beautiful new rooms in the renovated farmhouse. Good food waits, some home-grown, much from Yorkshire, perhaps cured sea trout with horseradish, slow cooked lamb with onion broth, chocolate with caramel and banana ice cream. The Dales wait to the west, the Moors to the east. Don't miss the Bowes museum in Barnard Castle, a jewel of the north.

Rooms	13 doubles: £140–£210. 1 suite for 2: £155–£185. 1 family room: £190–£310. Singles from £135. Cot available.
Meals	Lunch from £5.50. Dinner, 3 courses, £30–£35. Not Mon or Tue mid-Oct to mid-March. Sunday lunch from £12.50.
Closed	Never.

James & Rebecca Allison
The Coach House at Middleton Lodge
Middleton Tyas,
Richmond, DL10 6NJ

Tel	+44 (0)1325 377977
Email	info@middletonlodge.co.uk
Web	www.middletonlodge.co.uk/coach-house

Estbek House

A cute little find on the Whitby coast, a friendly restaurant with rooms ten paces from the beach at Sandsend. It's small, intimate and very welcoming. Tim cooks brilliantly, David talks you through his excellent wine list and passes on the local news. Cliffs rise to the north, the beach runs away to the south, ducks on the river occasionally waddle across the road. There's a terrace at the front for drinks in summer and a small bar on the lower ground, where you can watch Tim at work in his kitchen. Upstairs, two dining rooms swim in coastal light and come with stripped floors and white tablecloths. People come from miles around for the seafood – the lobster thermidor is a big draw – but carnivores are well looked after, so try home-smoked salmon with a gin and tonic jelly, stuffed pork tenderloin or Whitby crab, strawberry and champagne trifle. Bedrooms – smallish on the first floor, tiny on the second! – have crisp linen and shuttered windows. Breakfast is delicious, David's mum makes the marmalade. Cliff walks and the moors wait, and you can follow the river up to Mulgrave Castle.

Rooms	5 doubles: £200-£255. Price includes dinner for 2.
Meals	Dinner, 3 courses, included; non-residents about £35.
Closed	2 January – 12 February.

David Cross & Tim Lawrence
Estbek House
East Row, Sandsend,
Whitby, YO21 3SU

Tel	+44 (0)1947 893424
Email	info@estbekhouse.co.uk
Web	www.estbekhouse.co.uk

Entry 204   Map 6

Broom House at Egton Bridge

As lovely a place to stay on the moors as you could hope for. You wind your way in – up dale, down hill – with a carpet of purple heather in late summer and a golden fleece of bracken in autumn. As for this attractive house, it sits on the edge of a pretty village, with fine views of Esk Dale from the garden terrace. Inside, airy interiors are stylish and comfortable, the perfect tonic after a day in the hills. Downstairs, there's a sitting room with garden views, then a dining room for Michael's delicious breakfasts – Whitby kippers, Glaisdale bacon, smoothies from garden strawberries. In summer, you decant onto the terrace for birdsong with your bacon and eggs. Stylish rooms have warm colours, comfy beds, white cotton, perhaps a sofa or doors onto the terrace. All have fine bathrooms, one with a free-standing bath. By day you explore the moors, spin over to Whitby or try a leg of the coast-to-coast path, which passes outside. At night you follow the river into the village for dinner at one of its pubs. You couldn't be in better hands – Michael and Georgina look after you in style. Pure bliss. *Minimum stay: 2 nights at weekends.*

Rooms	6 doubles, 1 twin: £89-£137. 1 suite for 2, 1 suite for 4: £139-£200.
Meals	Two good pubs in village.
Closed	1 November – 1 March.

Georgina & Michael Curnow
Broom House at Egton Bridge
Broom House Lane, Egton Bridge,
Whitby, YO21 1XD
Tel   +44 (0)1947 895279
Email mail@broom-house.co.uk
Web   www.broom-house.co.uk

The Talbot Hotel

A 17th-century hunting lodge on the Fitzwilliam estate, not far from Castle Howard. It stands on the edge of town with Malton's streets on one side and country views on the other. Outside, there's a croquet lawn, a terrace for lunch, and paths that lead down to the river. Inside, an easy elegance abounds. A fire burns in the drawing room, you find fresh flowers, lovely art, the daily papers and cavernous sofas. Bedrooms have chic fabrics, warm colours and botanical prints on the walls. Several have the view, all have robes in gorgeous bathrooms. Now to the serious stuff – delicious local food. Malton, an ancient market town, is the food capital of Yorkshire, with a festival every May that was started by the estate. No surprise then to discover the hotel has two restaurants serving the best Yorkshire produce. They also run a cookery school and have food trails to follow – to pie shops, vineyards, local farms and breweries. Dinner, predictably, is a treat, perhaps pressing of Yorkshire duck, local lamb with an olive jus, coffee crème brûlée. There's a farmers' market every other Saturday, too. *Minimum stay: 2 nights at weekends.*

Rooms	23 doubles: £110–£190. 2 suites for 4, 1 suite for 2: £270–£320. Dinner, B&B from £100 p.p.
Meals	Lunch from £4.95. Bar meals from £10.95. Dinner, 3 courses, about £35. Sunday lunch from £20. Afternoon tea from £19.50.
Closed	Rarely.

David Macdonald
The Talbot Hotel
45–47 Yorkersgate,
Malton, YO17 7AJ

Tel	+44 (0)1653 639096
Email	reservations@talbotmalton.co.uk
Web	www.talbotmalton.co.uk

Entry 206   Map 6

Beck Hall

You'll feel instantly at home here with either Andy or Louise at the helm aided by a happy team of staff. Huge sliding glass doors allow guests to spill out from the restaurant into the pretty streamside garden. Malham is a mecca for walkers with the famous cove just under a mile away and Janet's Foss, Gordale Scar and the Tarn not much further. This is some of the most stunning and remote countryside in the UK and it's great for cycling as well as striding. Wild swimmers will be happy too with rivers, lakes and waterfalls to hurl themselves into. And dogs will love it all as much as their owners. Gird your loins for breakfasts of thick cut back bacon from the local farm shop, bangers from happy pigs and free-range eggs from the Dales. The restaurant, which is also open to the public, specialises in good, seasonal and local food cooked simply. Sleep well in comfortable bedrooms, all very different, all beautifully dressed, and dog-friendly too — beds, mats and bowls can be provided for your hound.

Rooms	21 doubles, 5 twins: £75–£135.
	5 family rooms for 3: £95–£135.
Meals	Lunch from £6.95.
	Dinner, 3 courses, £56.
	Afternoon tea from £14.95.
Closed	Never.

Andy & Louise Macbeth
Beck Hall
Cove Road, Malham, BD23 4DJ
Tel   +44 (0)1729 830729
Email   stay@beckhallmalham.com
Web   www.beckhallmalham.com

Channel Islands

The Georgian House

Alderney is pristine – miles of sandy beaches, ancient coastal forts, cliff-top walks and nature trails, wild flowers and migrating birds. It's a slice of heaven and where else to stay than this quirky island bolthole, part village inn, part restaurant with rooms, part friendly chic hotel. After 30 years holidaying here, Holly's family bought one of their favourite places, whipped it into shape and now it's the beating heart of the island, a magnet for locals and visitors alike. It sits on St Anne's cobbled high street, opposite the art-house cinema; filmgoers sneak over for drinks in the interval. Downstairs, the bar comes with wooden floors, an open fire and lots of gossip. An airy restaurant spills onto a sun-trapping courtyard in summer, a fine spot for the freshest seafood, delicious steaks, island ice creams. Bedrooms – some in the hotel, others across the road in Victoria House – are just the ticket: not huge, but deeply comfy, with lovely beds, the odd stone wall and cute bathrooms. Hire bikes, grab a picnic, laze about on the beach. Night skies amaze. A perfect island adventure.

Rooms	2 doubles, 2 twin/doubles: £70-£95. Singles from £45.
Meals	Light lunch from £6. Dinner, 3 courses, £25-£30.
Closed	Mid-January to mid-March.

Holly Fisher
The Georgian House
Victoria Street, Alderney, GY9 3UF

Tel	+44 (0)1481 822471
Email	info@georgianalderney.com
Web	www.georgianalderney.com

White House Hotel

Herm is unique, a tiny island run benignly by the 40 souls lucky enough to live on it. They keep things blissfully simple: no cars, no TVs, just a magical world of sea and sky, a perfect place to escape the city. A coastal path rings the island; high cliffs rise to the south, sandy beaches laze in the north, cattle graze the hills between. You get fabulous views at every turn – shimmering islands, pristine waters, yachts and ferries zipping about. There's a beach café, succulent gardens, an ancient church, even a tavern for excellent ales. Kids love it, so do parents, and the self-catering cottages are extremely popular. As for the hotel, it's a delightful base from which to explore the island. You'll find open fires, four-course dinners, a tennis court, then a pool in the garden to keep you cool. Spotless bedrooms are scattered about, some in the village's colour-washed cottages, others with balconies in the hotel. Most come in contemporary style, a few are warmly traditional, all have sunny colours, watery views, padded headboards and sparkling bathrooms. Hard to beat.

Rooms	28 twin/doubles: £138–£208.
	5 family rooms, 5 family rooms for 4:
	£128–£208. 2 singles: £72–£158.
	20 cottages for 6: from £343 per week.
	Dinner, B&B £97–£138 p.p.
Meals	Lunch from £5.
	Dinner, 4 courses, £28.50.
Closed	November – Easter.

Siôn Dobson Jones
White House Hotel
Herm Island, GY1 3HR

Tel	+44 (0)1481 750075
Email	hotel@herm.com
Web	www.herm.com

The Old Court House

This lovely hotel sits on St Aubin's harbour with views across the bay to St Helier and beyond. Outside, there's a sun-trapping terrace where you can watch sailing boats come and go. Inside, you find the star of the show, this beautiful house that mostly dates to 1610, but comes with a 13th-century granite staircase, too. Downstairs, there's an airy bar, then a restaurant split between two rooms. One has the feel of a galleon's dining quarters and featured as Diamond Lil's bar in the TV series *Bergerac*. The other, the old courthouse itself, has ancient walls of golden stone, then hanging lamps, painted beams and the original fireplace. Both are a delight, as is the food: lots of fresh seafood, delicious duck, sticky toffee pudding; a bistro below is popular with locals. Cute rooms have a soft, chic style: a wall of beautiful paper, white linen for Hypnos mattresses, super little bathrooms with big power showers. Two have slipper baths, one has a hot tub on a private terrace. As for Jersey, expect sandy beaches, gardens and galleries, castles and cliff-top walks. You can surf, sail and kayak, too.

Rooms	7 twin/doubles, 1 four-poster: £100–£300. 2 singles: £50–£75.
Meals	Lunch from £4.95. Dinner, 3 courses, about £35. Bistro: mains from £10.95. Sunday lunch from £14.95.
Closed	Never.

Jennifer Deahl
The Old Court House
Le Boulevard, St Aubin,
St Brélade, JE3 8AB

Tel	+44 (0)1534 746433
Email	info@oldcourthousejersey.com
Web	www.oldcourthousejersey.com

Photo:Killiecrankie House Hotel, entry 238

Scotland

The Creggans Inn

If you're looking for a small hotel in a great position with lovely rooms and excellent food, you'll find it here. There's a little history, too – the inn was once owned by the real James Bond. Sir Fitzroy Maclean was one of a cast of characters on whom Ian Fleming based his hero; the fact the Royal Navy send their big ships into Loch Fyne is purely coincidental. These days, life at the inn is decidedly restful. Views from the front stretch for miles, the loch eventually giving way to the distant peaks of the Kintyre peninsular. Inside, an airy elegance abounds. There's a first-floor sitting room with big views; a locals' bar which doubles as the clubhouse for the shinty team; then picture windows in the smart restaurant, where you dig into super food while watching the sun set, perhaps Ramsay haggis with whisky sauce, pot roast chicken with a thyme jus, bread and butter pudding with honey glazed figs. Comfy bedrooms have lots of style: warm colours, pretty fabrics, delicate wallpapers, robes in sparkling bathrooms; most have loch views. Castles and gardens, golf and boat trips wait.

Rooms	3 doubles, 11 twin/doubles: £100–£150. Singles £115.
Meals	Lunch from £5.95. Bar meals from £12.95. Dinner, 3 courses, from £25.
Closed	Never.

Archie & Gillian MacLellan
The Creggans Inn
Loch Fyne, Strachur,
Cairndow, PA27 8BX

Tel	+44 (0)1369 860279
Email	info@creggans-inn.co.uk
Web	www.creggans-inn.co.uk

The Manor House

A 1780 dower house for the Dukes of Argyll – their cottage by the sea. Built of local stone, it sits high on the hill with long views over Oban harbour to the Isle of Mull. It's a lovely small hotel with a stylish old-school feel: a roaring fire in the drawing room, beautiful tiles in the entrance hall, an elegant bay window in the bar, then a half-panelled dining room for excellent food. Attractive bedrooms have warm colours, fresh flowers, crisp linen, bowls of fruit and the odd antique. A couple are smaller, those with sea views have binoculars with which to scan the seven seas. Bathrooms are spotless, one has claw-foot bath. Dinner is a five-course feast, perhaps west coast sea bass, pea and ham soup, elderflower sorbet, saddle of lamb, sticky apple cake with vanilla ice cream; there's excellent home baking and Loch Fyne kippers for breakfast. Ferries leave for the islands from the bottom of the hill; watch them sail while digging into afternoon tea on the terrace. There's a computer for guests to use and you can climb up to McCaig's Tower to watch the sun set over the Hebrides. *Over 12s welcome.*

Rooms	9 doubles, 2 twins: £120–£260. Dinner, B&B from £87.50 p.p.
Meals	Lunch from £6. Dinner, 5 courses, £44.
Closed	Christmas.

Gregor MacKinnon
The Manor House
Gallanach Road,
Oban, PA34 4LS

Tel	+44 (0)1631 562087
Email	info@manorhouseoban.com
Web	www.manorhouseoban.com

The Pierhouse

The position here is unbeatable. You're at the end of the road, on the shores of Loch Linnhe, with views across to Lismore and rising mountains beyond. As for the Pierhouse – well, shipwrecked sailors would refuse rescue. Outside, there's a sun-trapping terrace from which to watch the odd boat chug past while digging into langoustines fresh from the waters around you. Interiors are just as good. Glass walls frame the view, there's a smart bar for a wee dram, a white-washed snug with sofas in front of a wood-burner, then, a restaurant for some of the best seafood on the west coast. Chic rooms have a wing to themselves, so expect deep peace. Those at the front have the view, all have an uncluttered Scandi feel with warm colours, padded bedheads, smart fabrics and robes in sparkling bathrooms. You get bowls of fruit, a sofa if there's room, crisp linen on comfy beds. There's lots to do: the ferry across to Lismore for fine walking, Ben Nevis, magical Ardnamurchan. As for the food, come back for oysters, scallops, lobster Thermidor or a rib-eye steak; the seafood platters are out of this world.

Rooms	4 doubles, 4 twin/doubles: £100–£275. 2 suites for 2: £145–£325. Extra beds: children aged 2-12 £30, 12+ £40.
Meals	Lunch from £4.95. Bar meals from £12.50. Dinner à la carte £30–£50.
Closed	25-26 December.

Nick & Nikki Horne
The Pierhouse
Port Appin, Appin, PA38 4DE

Tel	+44 (0)1631 730302
Email	reservations@pierhousehotel.co.uk
Web	www.pierhousehotel.co.uk

The Airds Hotel & Restaurant

This chic country-house hotel on the Appin peninsular stands above Loch Linnhe with views across the water to the Morvern Mountains. It came to life in 1750, an inn for passengers taking the paddle steamers up to the Caledonian canal. These days, it's one of the loveliest places to stay on the West Coast. Its whitewashed exterior gives no hint of the wonders within. You enter through a small conservatory, then find yourself in a world of smouldering fires, freshly cut flowers, beautiful wallpapers and soft sofas. Bedrooms are divine: beautiful fabrics, warm colours, Frette linen on Vi-Spring beds, sparkling marble bathrooms with robes; in short, the best of everything. Those at the front have the view, bigger rooms have sofas, some at the back have terraces, all spoil you rotten. Best of all is the exceptional food, perhaps West Coast langoustines with pea purée, sea bass with clams and a lemongrass cream, apple terrine with salted caramel and cinnamon doughnuts. There's a garden for croquet and afternoon tea with views to the water. Worth every penny.

Rooms	8 twin/doubles: £180-£325. 3 suites for 4, with sofabed: £365-£410. 1 cottage for 5: £595-£940 per week; 3-day stays from £210. Dinner, B&B from £145 p.p. Extra bed/sofabed £25 p.p.p.n.
Meals	Lunch from £7. Dinner, 5 courses £56; tasting menu £77. Sunday lunch £21.45.
Closed	Monday & Tuesday November to January.

	Shaun & Jenny McKivragan
	The Airds Hotel & Restaurant
	Port Appin, Appin, PA38 4DF
Tel	+44 (0)1631 730236
Email	airds@airds-hotel.com
Web	www.airds-hotel.com

Tiroran House

The setting is magnificent – 17 acres of gardens rolling down to Loch Scridian. Otters and dolphins pass through, buzzards and eagles glide above, red deer visit the garden. As for this 1850 shooting lodge, you'll be hard pressed to find a more comfortable island base. There are fires in the drawing rooms, fresh flowers everywhere, games to be played, books to be read. Airy bedrooms hit the spot: crisp linen, beautiful fabrics, the odd chaise longue; some have watery views, all have silence guaranteed. You eat in a smart dining room with much of the delicious food from the island or waters around it, perhaps mussel and oyster broth, saddle of lamb with carrot purée, chocolate torte with vanilla ice cream. Wander to the Whitetail Coffee Shop for afternoon tea. You're bang in the middle of Mull with lots to do: Tobermory, the prettiest town in the Hebrides; Calgary and its magical beach; day trips to Iona and its famous monastery; cruises to Staffa and Fingal's Cave. If you want to be more independent there are two self-catering cottages in the grounds.

Rooms	5 doubles, 5 twin/doubles: £175–£220.
Meals	Dinner, 4 courses, £48.
Closed	Rarely.

Laurence & Katie Mackay
Tiroran House
Tiroran, Isle of Mull, PA69 6ES

Tel	+44 (0)1681 705232
Email	info@tiroran.com
Web	www.tiroran.com

The Colonsay

Another fabulous Hebridean island, a perfect place to escape the world. Wander at will and find wild flowers in the machair, a golf course tended by sheep and huge sandy beaches across which cows roam. Wildlife is ever present, from a small colony of wild goats to a rich migratory bird population; the odd golden eagle soars overhead, too. At low tide the sands of the south give access to Oronsay. The island's 14th-century priory was one of Scotland's finest and amid impressive ruins its ornate stone cross still stands. As for the hotel, it brims with an easy style — airy interiors, stripped floors, fires everywhere, friendly staff. There's a locals' bar for a pint (and a brewery on the island), a pretty sitting room packed with books, a dining room for super food, a decked terrace for drinks in the sun. Bedrooms have local art, warm colours, lovely fabrics and the best beds; some have sea views, all have good bathrooms. Spin around on bikes, search for standing stones, lie in the sun and stare at the sky. There's a festival in May for all things Colonsay. Wonderful.

Rooms	4 doubles, 3 twins: £90–£160.
	1 family room for 4: £110–£150.
	1 single: £75–£85.
Meals	Lunch from £4.50. Packed lunch £7.
	Bar meals from £11.50.
	Dinner, 3 courses, about £25.
Closed	November, January (after New Year)
	& February.

Jane Howard
The Colonsay
Scalasaig, Isle of Colonsay, PA61 7YP
Tel   +44 (0)1951 200316
Email   hotel@colonsayestate.co.uk
Web   www.colonsayestate.co.uk

Glenisle Hotel

The Glenisle has a great tradition in hospitality – it was once the village jail! These days, it's the best place to stay on Arran – stylish and friendly with views across Lamlash Bay to Holy Island. Outside, there's a pretty terrace for lunch in the sun. Inside, you find stone walls, roaring fires, then books and games in a stylish sitting room. It's quirky, too – part of the bar was rescued from an old paddle steamer, and the hotel holds a Christmas festival at the end of November. There are two restaurants – one overlooking the garden, the other with mirrors on one wall – and the food hits the spot nicely: perhaps fish chowder with home-smoked mussels, coffee-crusted haunch of Arran venison; dark chocolate delice with walnut ice cream. Smart, airy rooms have comfy beds, colourful throws and robes in cute bathrooms. Two at the front look out to sea, the suite has a claw-foot bath overlooking the bay. As for Arran, it's a small-scale version of Scotland: mountains to the north, lush farmland to the south, then sandy beaches and the odd castle waiting on the coast. A perfect island base.

Rooms	5 doubles, 5 twin/doubles: £129-£195.
	1 suite for 2: £208-£228.
	2 singles: £95-£98.
Meals	Lunch & dinner £6-£38.
Closed	Never.

Anne Kennedy
Glenisle Hotel
Lamlash, Isle of Arran, KA27 8LY

Tel	+44 (0)1770 600559
Email	enquiries@glenislehotel.com
Web	www.glenislehotel.com

Knockinaam Lodge

Lawns run down to the Irish sea, roe deer come to eat the roses, sunsets turn the sky red. This beautiful hunting lodge is one of the loveliest country-house hotels in the land. The food is ambrosial, the panelled bar is home to 150 malts, and you'll find a level of service you rarely encounter in such far-flung corners of the realm. There's history, too. Churchill once stayed and you can sleep in his room, then climb into the deepest of baths and read his books. Immaculate interiors abound: gorgeous bedrooms, faultless bathrooms, a morning room where the scent of fresh flowers mingles with wood smoke. You'll find beautiful art, the daily papers, games and books galore. Outside, cliff walks lead over to Portpatrick, peregrine falcons circle on high, bluebells carpet the hills in spring. When it's stormy, waves crash all around. There's golf on the coast at Portpatrick, then Luce Bay for miles of sand. John Buchan knew the house and described it in *The Thirty-Nine Steps* as the house to which Hannay fled. Remote, beguiling, utterly spoiling – grand old Knockinaam is simply unmissable. *Pets by arrangement.*

Rooms	4 doubles, 5 twin/doubles: £300-£450.
	1 family room for 4: £360-£430.
	Singles £190-£330.
	Dinner, B&B £155-£230 per person.
Meals	Lunch, 2-3 courses, from £25.
	Dinner, 5 courses, included;
	non-residents £70.
Closed	Never.

David & Sian Ibbotson
Knockinaam Lodge
Portpatrick, Stranraer, DG9 9AD

Tel   +44 (0)1776 810471
Email   reservations@knockinaamlodge.com
Web   www.knockinaamlodge.com

Cavens

This small patch of heaven is a delight. You leave the world behind you, take the road south from Dumfries, and soon you're rolling through stunning country with hardly a soul in sight. Sunlight plays in the trees, ridges run down to lush fields, then suddenly you turn a corner and the Solway Firth is sparkling before your eyes. All you need now is somewhere wonderful to stay, somewhere small and beautiful, with kind owners on hand to usher you though to a chic sitting room before pouring you a gin and tonic, dishing up some wonderful food and showing you to your delightful quarters. Which is exactly what you find at Cavens, a small country house, where Jane and Angus look after guests in style. Two sitting rooms have open fires, period art and lots of books, then doors onto a garden where only birdsong will disturb you. As for the rooms, three are huge, one has the feel of a library, all have smart fabrics, super beds and garden views. Finally, dinner, an absolute delight, perhaps scallops with lime and Vermouth, venison with a port jus, a thin apple tart. Gardens, beaches and golf wait. Perfect.

Rooms	4 doubles, 1 twin: £200-£300. Singles £140-£200. Dinner, B&B £99-£160 per person. Extra bed/sofabed £40 per person per night.
Meals	Lunch from £6. Dinner, 3 course à la carte included; non-residents £35. Afternoon tea 'on the house.'
Closed	Rarely.

Jane & Angus Fordyce
Cavens
Kirkbean, Dumfries, DG2 8AA
Tel   +44 (0)1387 880234
Email   enquiries@cavens.com
Web   www.cavens.com

Trigony House Hotel and Garden Spa

A welcoming family-run hotel with good food and nicely priced rooms. There's a small spa in the garden, too, with rather good views from the hot tub. The house dates to 1700 and comes with Japanese oak panelling in the hall, a wood-burner in the sitting room and an open fire in the dining room, where doors open onto the terrace for dinner in summer. Adam cooks lovely rustic fare, perhaps prawns with coconut and coriander, saddle of roe venison, rhubarb and hazelnut crumble; a small, organic kitchen garden provides for the table in summer. Bedrooms – some big, some smaller – have warm colours, crisp linen, good beds and spotless bathrooms. A couple are dog-friendly, those at the back have the view, the suite opens onto a private garden. As for the spa, there's a treatment room, a sauna and a hot tub, so plenty of scope to recuperate after a day walking the Southern Upland Way or discovering the spectacular country between Moniaive and the Galloway Forest, a lost world of huge beauty you'll have to yourself. Don't miss Drumlanrig Castle for its gardens, walking trails and mountain bike tracks.

Rooms	4 doubles, 4 twin/doubles: £120-£140. 1 suite for 2: £165. Singles £90-£120. Dinner, B&B £95-£155 per person. Extra bed/sofabed £15 per person per night.
Meals	Lunch from £7.50. Dinner £25-£35. Afternoon tea £15.
Closed	24-26 December.

Adam & Jan Moore
Trigony House Hotel and Garden Spa
Closeburn, Thornhill, DG3 5EZ

Tel	+44 (0)1848 331211
Email	trigonyhotel@googlemail.com
Web	www.trigonyhotel.co.uk

Letham House

Why stay in the big smoke when you can live the life of Reilly at this baronial mansion that dates to 1645? It stands at the end of a tree-lined drive in 12 acres of woodland and gardens, with birdsong, strutting chickens and carpets of flowers to greet you. As for the house, it's a bona fide jaw-dropper. There's a wood-burner in the downstairs snug, then a crackling fire in a regal first-floor sitting room. You gather here for drinks before dinner (BYO), then spin down to the dining room, where you eat at one table in country-house style, feasting on delicious food, perhaps smoked haddock, chicken with tarragon, a chilled lemon mousse. After which you retire to delightful rooms and find huge beds, smart fabrics, antique furniture and garden flowers. Robes wait in fine bathrooms, three of which have claw-foot baths that overlook the garden. You're five miles from links golf at Gullane and North Berwick, ten miles from Edinburgh, with a bus that stops at the end of the drive. All of which would be blossom in the wind without Chris and Barbara, the undisputed stars of the show. Don't miss it. *Minimum stay: 2 nights at weekends between July – August.*

Rooms	5 twin/doubles: £130-£195.
	Extra beds: children free, adults £20.
Meals	Dinner, 3 courses, £35. BYO.
Closed	Never.

Barbara & Chris Sharman
Letham House
East Lothian,
Haddington, EH41 3SS

Tel	+44 (0)1620 820055
Email	stay@lethamhouse.com
Web	www.lethamhouse.com

23 Mayfield

A great base for all things Edinburgh. This attractive villa stands in the shadow of Arthur's Seat was built in 1868 for a coffee merchant. Outside, much prized, off-street parking waits. Inside, Victorian splendour at every turn: original fireplaces, ornate ceilings and a stained-glass window on the landing. The sitting room comes in dark period colours with newspapers on poles, gilt-framed pictures that hang on chains, and you can grab a drink from the honesty bar, then sink into a chesterfield sofa and watch an old movie or listen to trad jazz. Breakfast is even better. In winter you eat by candlelight, a candelabra on each table, and it's a feast of Scottish produce: porridge with honey, Arbroath smokies, rare breed sausages, marshmallow pancakes. Bedrooms have style and comfort in spades: white linen, excellent beds, fancy bathrooms, maybe wood floors or a brass chandelier. One has panelled walls, all have good art, iPod docks and smart TVs; the family room has a Nintendo Wii. You can jump on a bus and whizz into town, excellent restaurants wait nearby. A very friendly place. *Minimum stay: 2 nights at weekends May-September*

Rooms	4 twin/doubles, 2 four-posters: £110-£185. 1 family room for 4: £130-£200. Singles from £90.
Meals	Restaurants within half a mile.
Closed	24-26 December.

Ross Birnie
23 Mayfield
23 Mayfield Gardens,
Edinburgh, EH9 2BX
Tel   +44 (0)131 667 5806
Email   info@23mayfield.co.uk
Web   www.23mayfield.co.uk

94DR

Close to Holyrood and Arthur's Seat, this super-friendly designer B&B is not only popular for its contemporary style, but for Paul and John, who treat guests like friends and make sure you see the best of their city. A traditional Victorian exterior gives no hint of the chic interiors (updated regularly) that wait within. You'll find original floor tiles and ornate ceilings, but other than that it's a clean sweep of modern splendour: deep charcoal downstairs; pure white above. There's a sitting room with iPads in case you want to book a restaurant, then an honesty bar, an espresso machine and lots of handy guide books. Upstairs, stylish, well-priced bedrooms wait. Some are big with claw-foot baths, others smaller with walk-in power showers. All come with comfy beds, bathrobes, beautiful linen and fine contemporary art. The family suite (two rooms) has bunk beds and a PlayStation for kids. Delicious breakfasts are served in a conservatory overlooking the back garden, a memorable feast orchestrated by Paul, with lively conversation that travels the world. Majestic Edinburgh is yours to explore. *Minimum stay: 2 nights at weekends.*

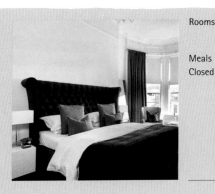

Rooms	3 doubles: £100-£145.
	2 suites for 2: £125-£225.
	1 family room for 4: £145-£190.
Meals	Restaurants within 0.5 miles.
Closed	Christmas, 4-23 January.

John MacEwan & Paul Lightfoot
94DR
94 Dalkeith Road,
Edinburgh, EH16 5AF

Tel	+44 (0)131 662 9265
Email	stay@94dr.com
Web	www.94dr.com

21212

A chic restaurant with rooms in Edinburgh's East End, with Holyrood Palace and the Botanic Gardens both close. Paul left his Michelin star down south, bought this Georgian townhouse, spent a fortune turning it into a 21st-century pleasure dome, then opened for business and won back his star. The house stands at the top of a hill with long views north towards the Firth of Forth. Inside, contemporary splendour waits. High ceilings and vast windows come as standard, but wander at will and find a cool first-floor drawing room, cherubs on the walls, busts and statues all over the place, even a private dining pod made of white leather. Stunning bedrooms have enormous beds, cool colours, fat sofas and iPod docks. Those at the front have the view, all have robes in magnificent bathrooms. As for the restaurant, the kitchen is on display behind a wall of glass and the food it produces is heavenly stuff, perhaps crab with caviar and scallops, chicken with pecan and pimiento, black cherry rice with cucumber and mint syrup. If that's not enough head up to Leith for afternoon tea on Royal Yacht Britannia. *Minimum stay: 3 days at New Year.*

Rooms	4 doubles: £115–£295.
Meals	Lunch from £28. Dinner, 3 courses, £70; 5-course tasting menu £85. Not Sunday or Monday.
Closed	Rarely.

Paul Kitching & Katie O'Brien
21212
3 Royal Terrace,
Edinburgh, EH7 5AB
Tel   +44 (0)131 523 1030
Email   reservations@21212restaurant.co.uk
Web   www.21212restaurant.co.uk

24 Royal Terrace

This stylish hotel is in the middle of an iconic row of Georgian townhouses facing a small park, so it's quiet even though you're in the heart of the city. Ask for a room on an upper floor for glorious views of the Firth of Forth. Impressive artworks are everywhere – the hotel's owner is a passionate collector – and the interiors are colourful and quirky, grand but not pretentious. Generous breakfasts with home baked cakes are served in the front room café and bar; stop by in the evening for a drink or sit out in the pretty terraced garden and, if you book ahead, treat yourselves to a champagne afternoon tea. You can walk, or hop on a bus, to castle, gardens, shops and museums. Paul Kitching's 21212 is a two-minute walk. *Minimum stay: 2 nights at weekends. Pets by arrangement.*

Rooms	6 twin/doubles: £90–£300.
	3 singles: £60–£180.
	2 family rooms, 3 suites: £90–£380.
	Extra sofabed for children £25 p.p.
Meals	Breakfast £14. Light bites from £4.50.
	Restaurants within 0.5 miles.
Closed	Christmas & one week in January.

Ivo Tamah
24 Royal Terrace
Edinburgh, EH7 5AH

Tel	+44 (0)131 297 2424
Email	reservations@24royalterrace.com
Web	www.24royalterrace.co.uk

Six Brunton Place

You step inside to find Doric columns and five-foot candelabra in the reception hall and that's just the start of it. This is a quirky, designer B&B in the centre of town, with Leith Walk to the north, Edinburgh Castle to the west and Arthur's Seat over the hill to the south. Hilary looks after her guests in great style, spills local secrets and offers a glass of wine 'on the house' every evening. The sitting room doubles as the breakfast room and comes with a bust in front of the wood burner, a long sofa that encourages idleness, then Chinese wood carvings and beautiful art. Bedrooms are scattered about, all filled with beautiful things. The garden suite is huge, a great base for families; the cute snug is perfect for those who travel light; one sweeps you back to a graceful past with dark walls and flamboyant curtains that fall from on high. All have coffee machines, flat-screen TVs and robes in excellent bathrooms. Breakfast is a treat: strong coffee, freshly squeezed orange juice, porridge, the full cooked works. Excellent restaurants wait on your doorstep. *Parking on London Road £4 a day.*

Rooms	3 doubles: £139–£179.
	1 suite for 4: £179–£239.
	Singles from £89.
Meals	Restaurants 2-minute walk.
Closed	23–28 December.

Hilary Scott
Six Brunton Place
6 Brunton Place, Edinburgh, EH7 5EG

Tel	+44 (0)131 623 6405
Email	contact@sixbruntonplace.com
Web	www.sixbruntonplace.com

The Bridge Inn at Ratho

This lovely inn sits in a small village directly above the Union Canal. Footpaths head west into the country, you can hire bikes and follow the tow path into Edinburgh, or jump on the pub's canal boat for a Sunday lunch cruise. If all that sounds too strenuous, then plonk yourself down on the terrace and watch the odd boat chug past while sipping a pint of good ale. Inside, the view is weather-proofed by big windows in the dining room. An easy style runs throughout. You'll find wood-burners, smart colours, a whisky bar, the odd sofa. In summer, there are barbecues on Friday nights, an ice cream shed in the garden, even a small festival in May with live bands and lots of beer. Rooms aren't huge, but hit the spot. They're stylish and comfy with smart beds and crisp linen. All but one has the view, three have walk-in power showers, one has a claw-foot bath. The airport is ten minutes away, but you're not on the flight path, so peace reigns. Finally, don't miss nearby Jupiter Artland in summer, a wonderland of beautiful things. Children are very welcome.

Rooms	3 doubles, 1 twin/double: £80–£120. Singles from £65.
Meals	Lunch & dinner £5–£35. Sunday lunch from £12.95.
Closed	Christmas Day.

Graham & Rachel Bucknall
The Bridge Inn at Ratho
27 Baird Road, Ratho, EH28 8RA

Tel	+44 (0)131 333 1320
Email	info@bridgeinn.com
Web	www.bridgeinn.com

The Ship Inn

There are few inns where you can sit on the terrace and watch a game of cricket on the beach below. But it's not beach cricket as you know it. This is serious stuff, played at low tide, and Mark Waugh, Viv Richards and Wasim Akram have all tried their hand. As for this cute little boutique inn, it's as good as any in the land, and it doubles as the pavilion… and the venue for post-match celebrations, no doubt. On sunny days, you decant onto the terrace for lunch in the sun and gaze across the Firth of Forth to Edinburgh's hills. Inside, contemporary rustic design mixes with roaring fires and the odd stone wall. Sofas and armchairs are scattered about, staff weave through the throng delivering delicious food – fish and seafood from local waters, lamb and beef from nearby farms, sinful puddings you can't resist; there are regular barbecues on the terrace, too. Smart rooms have seaside colours, crisp linen, coffee machines, fancy bathrooms with walk-in showers; those at the front have sea views, too. St Andrews waits for a round of golf, the Fife coastal path for excellent walks. A perfect place. *Pets by arrangement.*

Rooms	6 twin/doubles: £120–£185.
	Extra bed/sofabed £20 p.p. per night.
Meals	Lunch & dinner £5–£35.
	Sunday lunch from £12.95.
Closed	Christmas Day, 2 weeks in January.

Graham & Rachel Bucknall
The Ship Inn
The Toft, Elie, KY9 1DT

Tel	+44 (0)1333 330246
Email	info@bridgeinn.com
Web	www.shipinn.scot

15 Glasgow

This is a smart Glasgow address — bang in the middle of town, yet beautifully insulated from it. The house, grand Victorian, stands on an attractive square with communal gardens guests can enjoy. Inside, the feel is distinctly contemporary, despite a couple of Corinthian pillars in the entrance hall. It's all been beautifully renovated, and while technically you're in a B&B, the interiors here are a match for any boutique hotel. Downstairs, a vast sitting room has a couple of sofas in front of a fire. Bedrooms upstairs are no less generous. Those at the back are large, the suites at the front are huge. All come with king-size beds, crisp white linen, handmade bedheads and robes in gorgeous bathrooms. Suites have a few added extras: big sofas, beautiful windows, one has a double-ended bath overlooking the square. Breakfast is brought to you whenever you want. As for dinner, you'll find good restaurants nearby: the Finnieston for seafood and gin cocktails; the Gannet for a flat-iron steak; Ben Nevis for a wee dram and live folk music most nights. Don't miss the excellent Burrell Collection. *On-site parking.*

Rooms	3 doubles: £130–£150.
	2 suites for 2: £150–£170.
	Extra beds £20 p.p.
Meals	Restaurants on your doorstep.
Closed	Never.

Lorraine Gibson
15 Glasgow
15 Woodside Place, Glasgow, G3 7QL
Tel   +44 (0)141 332 1263
Email   rooms@15glasgow.com
Web   www.15glasgow.com

Kilcamb Lodge Hotel & Restaurant

Another stunning West Coast setting with Loch Sunart at the end of the garden and Glas Bheinn rising beyond. Kilcamb – a barracks during the Jacobite uprising – is a perfect base. There's a smart drawing room with an open fire, an elegant dining room for super food, a cool little brasserie for a spot of lunch, then a handful of deeply indulging rooms. A 12-acre garden rolls down to the water, where you might spot otters and seals. Ducks and geese fly overhead, if you're lucky you'll see eagles. Back inside, you'll find a whisky bar that does a good line in gin, then driftwood lamps, fresh flowers, good books and local art. You can eat in the restaurant or the brasserie, either a five-course tasting menu or something simpler, perhaps hand-dived scallops, Highland lamb, raspberry bavarois with champagne sorbet. Bedrooms have a country-house feel, some with a contemporary twist. You'll find warm colours, smart fabrics and excellent beds. One has a balcony, most have the view, all have spotless bathrooms, some with separate showers. Don't miss Ardnamurchan or Sanna Bay at the end of the road.

Rooms	2 doubles, 6 twin/doubles: £220–£380. 2 suites for 2: £300–£435. 1 family room for 4: £390–£435. Price includes dinner for 2.
Meals	Lunch from £7.50. Dinner, 3 courses included; non-residents £50; tasting menu £75. Sunday lunch £25. Afternoon tea £14.
Closed	January & 1st 2 weeks in December. Limited opening November & February.

David & Sally Ruthven-Fox
Kilcamb Lodge Hotel & Restaurant
Strontian, Acharacle, PH36 4HY

Tel	+44 (0)1967 402257
Email	enquiries@kilcamblodge.co.uk
Web	www.kilcamblodge.co.uk

Doune Knoydart

There is nowhere quite like Doune. You arrive by boat – there's no road in – a ferry across to Knoydart, the last great wilderness in Britain. You'll find mountain, sea and sky – a thrilling landscape of boundless peace and ever-changing light. It's a haven for wildlife – killer whales, Golden eagles, red grouse, otters and badgers – 120 species live here. As for Doune, it sits on the Sound of Sleat with views across to Skye. It's a tiny community of happily shipwrecked souls and Martin, Jane and Liz look after you with great generosity. The dining room is the hub, pine-clad from top to toe, with a stove to keep you warm and games in case it rains. The food is delicious – crab from the bay, roast lamb from the hill, chocolate tart with homemade ice-cream. Bedrooms along the veranda are delightfully simple; pine-clad cabins with mezzanine bunks for children, hooks for clothes, sparkling showers, armchairs for watching the weather. The walking is magnificent, boat trips can be arranged, the night sky astounds. There's a lodge for groups, too. A very special place, miss it at your peril. *Minimum stay: 3 nights.*

Rooms	2 doubles, 1 twin, each with mezzanine bed for children: £90. 1 single with separate shower: £33. Dinner, B&B £78-£95 p.p. (includes packed lunch).
Meals	Dinner £35.
Closed	October – March.

Martin & Jane Davies
Doune Knoydart
Knoydart, Mallaig, PH41 4PL

Tel	+44 (0)1687 462667
Email	martin@doune-knoydart.co.uk
Web	www.doune-knoydart.co.uk

Scourie Hotel

This famous old fishing hotel is a treat from top to toe. It's a quirky place run with great panache by the Campbell's, who bought it recently, refurbished in style and now it shines. It's supremely comfy – smart without being swanky, very much a country hotel. You'll find golden wallpapers, antique furniture, beautifully upholstered armchairs, then an open fire in the sitting room. It's a remarkably friendly place. Fishermen tend to come for the same week each year, re-booking when they leave, so everyone knows everyone but they also all go out of their way to welcome interlopers into the fold. There's great tradition, too; a board master allocates fishing beats each morning, a gong announces dinner. Stylish rooms have comfy beds, pretty fabrics, beautiful new bathrooms and no TVs; bliss. Dinner is a treat, perhaps ham hock terrine, fresh local salmon, profiteroles with chocolate sauce. There are two bars, a pretty garden, paths that lead down to the sea. This is a wildly beautiful corner of Scotland: spectacular walking, wildlife tours and golf all wait. You're on the North Coast 500, too.

Rooms	6 doubles, 6 twins: £145. 2 family rooms for 3: £160. 6 singles: £95. 1 chalet for 4: £200–£250. Dinner, B&B £105 per person. Extra bed/sofabed £35 per person per night.
Meals	Lunch from £4.95. Bar meals from £10. Dinner, 3 courses, £32.
Closed	7 October – 1 April.

Richard, Fiona & Charlotte Campbell
Scourie Hotel
Scourie, Lairg, IV27 4SX

Tel	+44 (0)1971 502396
Email	stay@scouriehotel.com
Web	www.scouriehotel.com

Mackay's Rooms

This is the north-west corner of Britain and it's utterly magical: huge skies, sandy beaches, aquamarine seas, cliffs and caves. You drive – or cycle – for mile upon mile with mountains soaring into the heavens and ridges sliding into the sea. If you like big, remote landscapes, you'll love it here; what's more, you'll pretty much have it to yourself. Mackay's – they have the shop, the bunkhouse and the garage, too – is the only place to stay in town, its earthy colours mixing with stone walls, open fires and stripped floors to great effect. Bedrooms (some big, others smaller) are extremely comfy. They come with big wooden beds and crisp white linen, while Fiona, a textiles graduate, has a fine eye for fabrics and upholstery. You also get excellent bathrooms, iPod docks, flat-screen TVs and DVD players. Breakfast sets you up for the day – grilled grapefruit, whisky porridge, venison sausages, local eggs – so head east to the beach, west for great golf or catch the ferry across to Cape Wrath and scan the sea for whales. There's surfing for the brave and the beautiful.

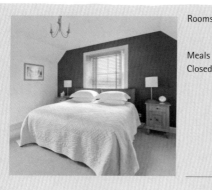

Rooms	6 doubles, 1 twin: £125–£189.
	4 cottages for 6: £800–£1600 per week.
	Singles £129.
Meals	Restaurants in village.
Closed	October – May. Cottages open all year.

Fiona Mackay
Mackay's Rooms
Durine, Durness, Lairg, IV27 4PN

Tel	+44 (0)1971 511202
Email	stay@visitdurness.com
Web	www.visitdurness.com

Viewfield House Hotel

It's a family affair, more like the Waltons than Hamlet, and the recent succession from father to daughter passed without a sword being drawn. Iona is now at the helm, but as Hugh is the only person on Skye who understands the plumbing system, he has been retained as a vital asset, and rightly so. As for their ancestral pile, it stands high above Portree Bay with long views across the Sound of Rassay. Twenty acres of gardens and woodland wrap around you; there's croquet on the lawn and a hill to climb for 360° views of peak and sea. Inside, aristocratic fixtures and fittings come as standard: hunting trophies, cases filled with curios, a grand piano and open fire in the drawing room. Bedrooms have a country-house feel: colourful fabrics, crisp linen, pretty furniture, sea views from those at the front; bathrooms do the job nicely and are in the throes of refurbishment. Majestic Skye waits: mountains, sea lochs and beaches, wildlife, castles and distilleries. Dinner is available by arrangement, but there are good restaurants in Portree, too. Highland porridge for breakfast is a treat. An old-school, island delight.

Rooms	4 doubles, 4 twin/doubles, 1 twin: £129-£200. 2 singles: £77-£90. Dinner, B&B £90-£125 p.p..
Meals	Dinner, 3 courses, £25-£30, price dependent on pre-booking. Packed lunch, £9.
Closed	Mid-Oct to Easter.

Iona Macdonald & Jasper Buxton
Viewfield House Hotel
Viewfield Road, Portree, IV51 9EU
Tel   +44 (0)1478 612217
Email   info@viewfieldhouse.com
Web   www.viewfieldhouse.com

Coruisk House

You follow the road for 15 miles through magnificent landscapes — down the glen, around the loch and over the mountain to Elgol. Your reward is this little restaurant with rooms waiting at the end of the track. A rustic style has conquered every corner, ambrosial food flies from the kitchen, a glass of prosecco is yours on arrival. The breakfast room runs along the front of the house with a string of windows that frame the view. You'll find hanging lamps, up-cycled furniture, lime-washed walls and a painted settle. Airy rooms have big beds, mohair throws, white linen, robes in quirky bathrooms. New rooms in the cottage next door have the same delicious style and the odd claw-foot bath. As for Iain's glorious food, you eat in the restaurant, where a wood-burner keeps things cosy, perhaps crab brûlée with lobster bisque, Highland beef with braised oxtail, ginger steamed pudding with Drambuie ice cream. Drop down to Elgol harbour, where Bonnie Prince Charlie fled for his life, and gaze upon the mighty Cuillin rising from the sea. Stags roam the hills, boat trips can be arranged. Heaven. *Over 14s welcome. Pets by arrangement.*

Rooms	3 doubles: £150–£250.
	1 suite for 4: £370–£400.
Meals	Dinner £40–£45.
Closed	20 October – 28 February.

Iain Roden & Clare Winskill
Coruisk House
26 Elgol,
Elgol, IV49 9BL

Tel	+44 (0)1471 866330
Email	info@coruiskhouse.com
Web	coruiskhouse.com

Culdearn House

Grantown is a great base for Highland flings. You can fish the Spey, jump on the whisky trail, check out a raft of castles, even ski in Aviemore. Loch Ness is close, as is Royal Deeside, there's golf everywhere and the walking is divine; in short, expect to be busy. As for Culdearn, it stands in a row of five identical houses that were built in 1860 by Lord Seafield, one for each of his daughters. These days it's a lovely small hotel where William and Sonia look after guests with unstinting kindness. There's an open fire and facing sofas in the smart sitting room, panelled windows and a marble fireplace in the dining room, then stylish bedrooms that offer the sort of comfort you hope for after a day in the hills. You get the comfiest beds, the crispest linen, then decanters of sherry, fresh flowers and robes for spotless bathrooms. Back downstairs, William looks after a tempting wine list and 60 malts, while Sonia whisks up delicious four-course dinners, perhaps West Coast scallops, bramble sorbet, fillet of beef, a walnut and maple syrup parfait. Don't miss the ospreys at Boat of Garten. *Over 10s welcome.*

Rooms	4 doubles, 1 twin/double, 1 twin: £160–£180. Singles £120–£150.
Meals	Dinner, 4 courses, £48.
Closed	Rarely.

Sonia & William Marshall
Culdearn House
Woodlands Terrace, Speyside,
Grantown on Spey, PH26 3JU

Tel	+44 (0)1479 872106
Email	enquiries@culdearn.com
Web	www.culdearn.com

Dunalastair Hotel Suites

Rannoch Moor is one of those magical places where the hand of man has hardly touched the landscape. You're encircled by hills, with a couple of lochs thrown in for good measure. As for the road, it peters out at the station 20 miles west, where the London train stops and passengers disembark, bicycle in hand. Some, very sensibly, spin down to this chic hotel and check in for a night or two of luxury. It was built in 1860 and now a recent renovation has added 21st-century comfort and style. You'll find a roaring fire in the hall, a dram or two in the wee bar, colourful art in the big sitting room, then delicious food in the restaurant, perhaps Scottish scallops, loin of roe deer, apple parfait with rosemary and sage. In summer you decant into the courtyard for breakfast, lunch and dinner. Chic suites offer more than most: the best beds, sofas and smart TVs, well-stocked kitchenettes, then dining tables for room service. Swish bathrooms have walk-in showers, some have baths, too. Kind staff are the best, nothing is too much trouble. You can kayak, fish, hire bikes or bag a munro. *Minimum stay: 2 nights July – August.*

Rooms	22 suites for 2, 8 suites for 4, 2 suites for 6: £155–£299.
Meals	Lunch from £6. Mains from £7.95. Dinner, 3 courses, £35. Afternoon tea £18. Food served all day.
Closed	Never.

Richard Deak
Dunalastair Hotel Suites
1 The Square,
Kinloch Rannoch, PH16 5PW

Tel	+44 (0)1882 580444
Email	bookings@dunalastairhotel.com
Web	www.dunalastairhotel.com

The Inn at Loch Tummel

You weave through the forest, then arrive at this 200-year-old inn to find views of field, hill, loch and sky. It's a magical spot, with a small garden to the front that drinks it all in. As for the inn, Alice and Jade rescued it from neglect, poured in love and money and now it shines. Interiors mix contemporary flair with Highland charm, the very definition of rustic chic. You'll find a cool little bar, painted beams and a wood-burner in the restaurant, then a first-floor sitting room with fat sofas, books and games, goatskin rugs and Jade's guitar. Bedrooms are a treat: chic fabrics, beautiful beds, cool colours, woollen throws. Some are big, none are small, one is dog friendly, most have the view. All have good art, decanters of whisky and spotless bathrooms, some with walk-in showers. By day you explore the hills, whizz down mountain bike trails or climb Schiehallion, the local munro. At night you return for delicious food, perhaps calamari with chilli and lemon, rack of local lamb, an espresso brownie with beetroot meringue. Queen's View, up the road, has one of the best views in Scotland. *Children over 5 welcome.*

Rooms	2 doubles, 4 twin/doubles: £105–£155.
Meals	Dinner with wine £27.
Closed	Rarely.

Alice & Jade Calliva
The Inn at Loch Tummel
Queen's View,
Strathtummel, PH16 5RP

Tel   +44 (0)1882 634317
Email   info@theinnatlochtummel.com
Web   www.theinnatlochtummel.com

Killiecrankie House Hotel

No Highland fling would be complete without a night at Killiecrankie. Henrietta runs the place with great charm and has spent the last ten years pouring in love and money; now it shines. Outside, gardens galore: one for roses, another for vegetables, and a fine herbaceous border. Further afield, you'll find much to please: Loch Tummel, Rannoch Moor and magnificent Glenshee, over which you tumble for the Highland Games at Braemar. Return to the indisputable comforts of a smart country hotel: tartan in the dining room, 52 malts at the bar, views at breakfast of red squirrels climbing garden trees. There's a snug sitting room where a fire burns in winter; in summer doors open onto the garden. Delightful bedrooms come in different shapes and sizes. All are smart with pretty linen, warm colours, chic fabrics and lovely views. Dinner is predictably delicious, perhaps pea and mint soup, Highland venison, sticky toffee pudding. There's porridge with cream and brown sugar for breakfast. Castles, hills and distilleries wait. A great wee place with staff who care. *Minimum stay: 2 nights at weekends. Pets by arrangement.*

Rooms	3 doubles, 5 twin/doubles: £250–£340. 2 singles: £140–£170. Price includes dinner for 2.
Meals	Lunch from £4.50. Dinner included; non-residents £42.
Closed	3 January – 23 March.

Henrietta Fergusson
Killiecrankie House Hotel
Killiecrankie,
Pitlochry, PH16 5LG

Tel	+44 (0)1796 473220
Email	enquiries@killiecrankiehotel.co.uk
Web	www.killiecrankiehotel.co.uk

Craigatin House & Courtyard

Craigatin is one of those lovely places where beautiful rooms have attractive prices and hands-on owners go out of their way to make your stay special. It stands peacefully in two acres of manicured gardens on the northern shores of town; good restaurants are a short stroll. Smart stone exteriors give way to warmly contemporary interiors, where beautiful windows flood rooms with light. There are shutters in the breakfast room, which overflows into an enormous conservatory where sofas wait in front of a wood-burner and walls of glass open onto the garden. Big uncluttered bedrooms – some in the main house, others in converted stables – are super value for money. Expect Farrow & Ball colours, comfy beds, crisp white linen, padded bedheads and pretty shower rooms. Breakfast offers the full cooked works and tempting alternatives, perhaps smoked haddock omelettes or apple pancakes with grilled bacon and maple syrup. As for Pitlochry – gateway to the Highlands – it's a vibrant town with lots to do: castles and mountains, lochs and forests, its famous Festival Theatre. You're on the whisky trail, too. *Minimum stay: 2 nights at weekends.*

Rooms	11 doubles, 2 twins: £109–£118.
	1 suite for 2: £136. Singles £99–£126.
Meals	Restaurants within walking distance.
Closed	Christmas.

Martin & Andrea Anderson
Craigatin House & Courtyard
165 Atholl Road,
Pitlochry, PH16 5QL

Tel	+44 (0)1796 472478
Email	enquiries@craigatinhouse.co.uk
Web	www.craigatinhouse.co.uk

Knockendarroch Hotel & Restaurant

This grand old house on a hill was built in 1880, then sold in 1910 for £100! It is also the birthplace of the Pitlochry Festival Theatre, the plays originally performed in the garden. These days it's simply a lovely place to stay with views from the front that shoot across the valley to forested hills. Inside, you find original tiles in the hall, a double sitting room with two fires, a whisky bar for a wee dram, a wallpapered restaurant with views of Ben Vrackie and plenty of original contemporary art. Good paths lead up through forest and moorland for big Highland views, not a bad way to work up an appetite for some very good food, perhaps fillet of hake with chilli and lemongrass, Perthshire lamb with parsnip purée, elderflower panna cotta with pear sorbet. Bedrooms are lovely, it really doesn't matter which you choose, though the big ones at the front do have exceptional views. You'll find comfy beds, smart fabrics, tartan throws and padded headboards, perhaps a cushioned window seat or a sofa if there's room. Two have balconies, most have binoculars to scan the hills. There's a drying room for wet gear, too. *Minimum stay: 2 nights at weekends. Over 10s welcome.*

Rooms	12 twin/doubles: £140–£195. Dinner, B&B £100–£173 p.p.
Meals	Lunch from £5. Dinner, 3 courses, £25; £42 non-residents.
Closed	20 December – 6 February.

Struan & Louise Lothian
Knockendarroch Hotel & Restaurant
Higher Oakfield, Pitlochry, PH16 5HT
Tel +44 (0)1796 473473
Email bookings@knockendarroch.co.uk
Web www.knockendarroch.co.uk

The Meikleour Arms

Much of the food you eat in the restaurant of this Perthshire country inn comes from the estate — vegetables and herbs grown in the walled garden, scallops hand-dived on the west coast and venison from the Meikleour Forest. You can also sample some quirky finds from the less well known vineyards in Bordeaux. Walk to the river for a morning's salmon or trout fishing on the Tay — book a fly-fishing lesson with the head ghillie. Spot ospreys, otters, kingfishers. The Blairgowrie Golf Course is a five-mile drive, while three others are within 30 miles. Book a tour of a couple of whisky distilleries too — Blair Athol and Edradour are in Pitlochry (a 40-minute drive). Scone Palace, Glamis and Balmoral are all within reach. You stay in the 19th-century coaching inn or the serviced cottages in the grounds — a short drive or walk from the main building. The cottages have small kitchens, but you can wander over for breakfast in the restaurant each morning. *Minimum stay: 2 nights in the cottages.*

Rooms	11 doubles: £100–£130. 2 cottages for 2, 2 cottages for 4, 1 cottage for 6: £110–£225.
Meals	Light bites about £8. Lunch & dinner à la carte, 2 courses, about £20.
Closed	Never.

Claire Mercer Nairne
The Meikleour Arms
Meikleour, PH2 6EB
Tel +44 (0)1250 883206
Email claire@meikleour.com
Web www.meikleourarms.co.uk

Ardeonaig Hotel

This magical small hotel sits on the quiet side of Loch Tay with gardens that run down to the water and mountains that rise beyond. Silence and mother nature are the chief ingredients. You weave along a single-track lane, leaving the world behind, then find whitewashed walls adorned with hanging baskets and you've arrived. Inside, there's an elegant sitting room with a peat fire, a snug bar for a wee dram, a pretty restaurant that overlooks the burn. Outside, there's a courtyard garden for afternoon tea in the sun. Bedrooms are a delight, some smaller, others bigger, all with big beds, crisp linen, a sofa if there's room. White walls soak up the light, several have the view, one has a wood-burner, garden suites are huge; all have robes in spotless bathrooms. There's lots to do: you can kayak, bag a couple of munros, zoom down mountain-bike trails or just take to the hills and find ancient burial grounds, Rob Roy's hideouts and a ruined medieval castle. Dinner is a treat, perhaps home-smoked salmon, Perthshire lamb, peaches with whisky and heather. There's a music festival in Killin in June.

Rooms	8 doubles, 3 twin/doubles: £120–£200. 7 suites for 2: £175–£250. Dinner, B&B from £95 p.p. Singles from £110. Extra bed available.
Meals	Lunch from £6. Dinner, £31–£37.50. Sunday lunch from £16. Afternoon tea £6.50.
Closed	Never.

Ian Hitchens
Ardeonaig Hotel
South Loch Tay Side,
Near Killin, FK21 8SU

Tel	+44 (0)1567 820351
Email	info@ardeonaighotel.co.uk
Web	www.ardeonaighotel.co.uk

Monachyle Mhor

Monachyle is unique – a designer hotel on a remote hill farm that started life as a B&B. Today it's one of the hippest places to stay in Scotland and it's still run by the same family with the children at the helm. Dick farms, Melanie designs the magical rooms, Tom cooks some of the best food in Scotland. It sits in 2,000 acres of blissful silence at the end of the track with the Trossachs circling around you and Loch Voil shimming below. Sheep graze, buzzards swoop, the odd fisherman tries his luck. Inside, there's a cool little bar, a fire in the sitting room, then a slim restaurant that drinks in the view. Bedrooms ooze 21st-century chic: big beds, cool colours, fabulous design, hi-tech gadgets. Bathrooms are equally good, perhaps a deluge shower in a granite steam room or claw-foot baths with views down the glen. Loft-house suites are enormous, but the smaller rooms are lovely, too. Dinner is a five-course feast with beef, lamb, pork and venison all off the farm. Rob Roy lived in the glen, you can visit his grave. The hotel holds a festival in May – fabulous food and cool Scottish tunes. *Please pre-book meals at hotel reception*

Rooms	9 twin/doubles: £195–£215. 5 suites for 2: £265. 1 family room for 4: £195–£265.
Meals	Lunch from £5.50. Dinner, 5 courses, £50. Sunday lunch £32.
Closed	Two weeks in January.

	Tom Lewis Monachyle Mhor Balquhidder, Lochearnhead, FK19 8PQ
Tel	+44 (0)1877 384622
Email	monachyle@mhor.net
Web	monachylemhor.net

Mhor 84

The entirely benevolent expansion of the Mhor empire has mastered the Midas touch, turning this old roadside inn into the coolest motel in the land. Outside, the glen shoots down to Loch Voil, with mountains to climb and bike tracks to follow. Inside, chic white minimalism mixes with warm Scottish tradition, a perfect blend of relaxed 21st-century living. There's style and humour in equal measure – boarded floors, tractor seat bar stools, curios hanging on the walls, the odd sofa for afternoon tea. Fires roar, cake stands bulge, happy staff weave through the throng delivering fabulous food that you eat at old school tables – porridge with honey for breakfast, sourdough and hummus for lunch, Scotch rarebit, Tyree lobster and plum crumble for dinner. There's live folk music every Thursday – Ewan MacPherson of Shooglenifty often plays – and a fine selection of malts if you fancy a dram. Simple bedrooms have white walls, contemporary art, small armchairs and honest prices; spotless bathrooms are 1980s originals, all part of the fun. There's a games room, too, with a juke box and pool table.

Rooms	2 doubles, 4 twin/doubles: £70–£80. 1 family room for 4: £80–£110.
Meals	Breakfast from £4.50. Lunch from £3.90. Dinner, 3 courses, £25–£35.
Closed	Christmas Day.

Dugald McGarry
Mhor 84
Balquhidder,
Lochearnhead, FK19 8NY

Tel	+44 (0)1877 384646
Email	motel@mhor.net
Web	mhor84.net

Photo: Dunalastair Hotel Suites, entry 236

Cringletie House

Cringletie's splendours are hard to miss. You're wrapped up in 65 acres of beautiful grounds with daffodils that erupt in spring, cows that graze in lush fields and a peaceful walled garden for a game of boules. Pheasants strut, buzzards circle, views roll over nearby hills. As for the house, it dates to 1860, its playful turrets giving it a soft grandeur. Inside, you get the full works: an open fire in the hall, then a fine old staircase that sweeps you up to a striking first-floor dining room that has the feel of an 18th-century gentleman's club; expect panelled walls, vintage wallpapers and a spectacular muralled ceiling. There's a sitting room up here, too – equally grand, with fat sofas in front of the fire. Bedrooms are scattered about. Some downstairs open onto the garden, those at the top have the best views. It doesn't matter which you go for, they're all lovely, with warm colours, crisp linen, comfy beds and excellent bathrooms. Take to the hills, follow the Tweed or scoot up to Edinburgh; it's less than an hour by car.

Rooms	12 twin/doubles: £135–£245.
	1 suite for 2: £235–£265.
	1 cottage for 6: £235–£465.
Meals	Lunch from £9.50.
	Dinner, 3 courses, £37.50.
	Sunday lunch £22.50.
	Afternoon tea from £18.50.
Closed	3–25 January.

Jeremy Osbourne
Cringletie House
Edinburgh Road,
Peebles, EH45 8PL

Tel	+44 (0)1721 725750
Email	enquiries@cringletie.com
Web	www.cringletie.com

Windlestraw

A small country house with lovely interiors and beautiful views down the Tweed Valley. Hills rise, deer roam, osprey glide through the afternoon sky. John and Sylvia came back from Dubai to do their own thing and have been hard at work presiding over a chic refurbishment. Fires roar, a grand piano waits to be played, there's a sun-trapping terrace for afternoon tea. You find a conservatory sitting room filled with books and curios, a panelled dining room for super food, then binoculars with which to scan the valley – sunsets turn the hills orange. Country-house bedrooms have a warm contemporary style: smart colours, comfy beds, sofas in the bigger rooms, fine views from those at the front. Spotless bathrooms do the trick: one has a claw-foot bath, bigger rooms have robes. Good food waits downstairs, perhaps scallops from Eyemouth, local lamb, an irresistible tarte tatin. There's lots to do: walking, fishing, mountain biking, even kayaking on the Tweed; if you try your hand on Pebbles golf course, the views may well be better than your game! There's a literary festival at Traquair House in August, too.

Rooms	5 doubles: £200–£220.
	1 suite for 2: £280. Singles from £125.
	Extra beds for children £15. Cots free.
Meals	Dinner, 4 courses, £55.
Closed	10 December – 10 February.

John & Sylvia Matthews
Windlestraw
Galashiels Road,
Walkerburn, EH43 6AA
Tel   +44 (0)1896 870636
Email   stay@windlestraw.co.uk
Web   www.windlestraw.co.uk

The Allanton Inn

Allanton, population 100. Welcome to the sleepy back of beyond, an untouched corner of the rural idyll that most people skip on their rush north. Well, there's no rush here, just patchwork fields, rolling hills and the river Tweed pottering off to the coast. As for this cute little inn, it's a great base from which to explore. The style is charming, the locals friendly, the prices lovely, the food a treat. It sits on the only street in town with a garden that backs onto open country; in summer you can have lunch in the sun while watching the farmer plough his fields. Inside, home-spun interiors have colour and style. There's an open-plan feel, the airy bar flowing into a half-panelled restaurant. You'll find a smouldering fire, fresh flowers, good art, local ales. Rooms have an easy style: padded bedheads, good bathrooms, Farrow & Ball colours. A couple are big, those at the back have the view. Super local food waits downstairs, perhaps an Eyemouth fish platter, rump of local lamb, lavender and raspberry brûlée. There's local honeycomb at breakfast, too. You can fish, walk, play a bit of golf. Perfect.

Rooms	3 doubles, 2 twin/doubles: £85–£105. 1 family room for 4: £110–£155. Singles from £70.
Meals	Lunch from £6.75. Dinner, 3 courses, £25–£35. Sunday lunch from £12.50.
Closed	Christmas.

William & Katerina Reynolds
The Allanton Inn
Allanton, By Duns, TD11 3JZ

Tel	+44 (0)1890 818260
Email	info@allantoninn.co.uk
Web	www.allantoninn.co.uk

Scarista House

All you need to know is this: Harris is one of the most beautiful places in the world. Beaches of white sand that stretch for a mile or two are not uncommon. If you bump into another soul, it will be a delightful coincidence, but you shouldn't count on it. The water is turquoise, coconuts sometimes wash up on the beach. The view from Scarista is simple and magnificent: field, ridge, beach, water, sky. Patricia and Tim are the kindest people. Their home is island heaven: peat fires, rugs on painted floors, books everywhere, a first-floor drawing room that floods with Harris light. Country-house bedrooms have warm colours and stylish bathrooms. There are walking sticks and wellington boots to help you up the odd hill, and a set of golf clubs by the front door in case you wish to play (the view from the first tee is one of the best in the game). Kind staff may speak Gaelic. The food is exceptional, perhaps quail with an armagnac mousse, Harris langoustine with garlic and butter, tarte tatin with cinnamon ice cream. Don't miss Uig Sands or the standing stones at Callanish. A perfect place. *Pets by arrangement.*

Rooms	2 doubles, 1 twin: £207–£245.
	2 suites for 2, 1 family room for 4:
	£233–£245. Singles £153.
Meals	Dinner, 3 courses, £44.
	Packed lunch from £7.50.
Closed	Christmas, New Year,
	1 January – 28 February.

Patricia & Tim Martin
Scarista House
Scarista, Isle of Harris, HS3 3HX
Tel   +44 (0)1859 550238
Email timandpatricia@scaristahouse.com
Web   www.scaristahouse.com

Wales

Photo: The Manor Town
House, entry 268

Wright's Food Emporium

This is one of those wonderful places you come across once every ten years, the sort that makes no effort to conform and so brings to life a quirky style that's delightful and authentic. It's a temple to local food – a café, a restaurant, a deli, and a wine shop, though it's not often you can sit in a wine shop, stick on a Bob Dylan LP and dig into glorious food washed down by organic wines. Its legion of fans come from near and far, with staff weaving through the throng to deliver manna from heaven. One room leads to another, all designed to please. You'll find tables crammed with delicious cakes; soups simmering away on the range; a fire and original flagstones in the back room; then a swish lean-to stuffed with curios and pot plants that opens onto a terrace. As for the deli, 'we sell the food we like' says Maryann of her culinary Aladdin's Cave. It's all fresh and local – breads, meat, eggs, vegetables, chutneys, jams, even chocolate. Two rustic-chic cottages are a steal for those wise enough to linger. Both come with kitchens you probably won't use. Don't think, just come, happiness waits. *Short breaks available.*

Rooms	1 cottage for 4: £110–£280; £700–£875 per week. 1 cottage for 6: £110–£280; £760–£1250 per week.
Meals	Lunch from £6. Dinner, 3 courses, £25–£30. Last orders for food: 7pm; 9pm Fri & Sat.
Closed	Tuesdays.

Joel, Simon & Maryann Wright
Wright's Food Emporium
The Golden Grove Arms,
Llanarthne, SA32 8JU

Tel	+44 (0)1558 668929
Email	maryann@wrightsfood.co.uk
Web	www.wrightsfood.co.uk

Ty Mawr Country Hotel

Pretty rooms, attractive prices and delicious food make this welcoming country house hard to resist. It sits in a very peaceful spot. You drive over hills, drop into the village, then wash up at this 16th-century stone house that comes in soft yellow. Outside, a sun-trapping terrace laps against a trim lawn, which in turn drops into a passing river. Gentle eccentricities abound: croquet hoops take odd diversions, logs are piled high like giant beehives, a seat has been chiselled into a tree trunk. Inside, original stone walls and low beamed ceilings give a warm country feel. There are fires everywhere – one in the attractive sitting room that overlooks the garden, another in the dining room that burns on both sides. Excellent bedrooms are all big. You get big beds, warm colours, crisp linen, good bathrooms. Some have sofas, all are dog-friendly, three overlook the garden. Back downstairs, the bar doubles as reception, while Welsh art on the walls is for sale. Steve's cooking is the final treat, perhaps Cardigan Bay scallops, organic Welsh beef, calvados and cinnamon rice pudding. Top stuff. *Over 10s welcome.*

Rooms	3 doubles, 3 twin/doubles: £115–£130. Singles £80.
Meals	Dinner £25–£30.
Closed	Rarely.

Annabel & Steve Thomas
Ty Mawr Country Hotel
Brechfa, SA32 7RA

Tel   +44 (0)1267 202332
Email   info@wales-country-hotel.co.uk
Web   www.wales-country-hotel.co.uk

Penbontbren

You're lost in lovely hills, yet only three miles from the sea. Not that you're going to stray far. These gorgeous suites don't just have wonderful prices, they're heaped with comforts, too – this is a great spot to come and do nothing at all. Richard and Huw have thought it all through. You get crockery and cutlery, kettles and fridges, then you're encouraged to bring your own wine or to buy provisions from the farm shop for lunch. As for the suites, expect big beds, super bathrooms, sofas and armchairs in pretty sitting areas, then doors onto semi-private terraces – perfect for lunch in summer. You get iPod docks, flat-screen TVs, robes and White Company lotions, too. The new garden room is a little smaller than the others, but has a big terrace to compensate. Breakfast is served in the main house – the full Welsh works. Beautiful hills, sandy beaches, Cardigan and magical St Davids all wait. Good local restaurants are on hand: lobster from the sea, lamb from the hills. Don't miss The Shed in Porthgain for excellent fish and chips. A great place to unwind with discounts for longer stays. *Minimum stay: 2 nights in high season.*

Rooms	6 suites for 2: £90–£130. 1 cottage for 7: £650–£1150. Singles £85–£99.
Meals	Restaurants within 3 miles.
Closed	Christmas.

Richard Morgan-Price & Huw Thomas
Penbontbren
Glynarthen, Llandysul, SA44 6PE

Tel	+44 (0)1239 810248
Email	contact@penbontbren.com
Web	www.penbontbren.com

Escape Boutique B&B

A designer B&B with lovely rooms, attractive prices and some seriously fancy bathrooms. The house stands high on the hill, away from the crowds, a short stroll from the buzz of town and its two-mile beach. This is a 19th-century mill owner's villa and its fine old windows, sparkling wood floors and carved fireplace bear testament to its Victorian roots. Other than that it's a clean sweep of funky interiors. Sam and Gaenor scoured Europe for their eclectic collection of colourful retro furniture that fills the rooms — orange swivel chairs, iconic G-plan sofas, beautiful beds wrapped in crisp white linen. You'll find cow-hide rugs, funky wallpapers, big views from rooms at the front. All come with flat-screen TVs, Blu-ray DVD players and iPod docks. Bathrooms are excellent: one room has a shower for two, another has a copper bath in the room. Downstairs, there's an honesty bar in the sitting room, while delicious breakfasts are served in an attractive dining room. Good food waits in town — the Seahorse for fish, Mamma Rosa for Italian. Great Orme waits above for big views of the bay. *Minimum stay: 2 nights at weekends.*

Rooms	8 doubles, 1 twin/double: £99–£149. Singles from £80.
Meals	Restaurants within walking distance.
Closed	Christmas.

Sam Nayar & Gaenor Loftus
Escape Boutique B&B
48 Church Walks, Llandudno, LL30 2HL

Tel	+44 (0)1492 877776
Email	info@escapebandb.co.uk
Web	www.escapebandb.co.uk

Entry 253   Map 5

Osborne House

Osborne House – originally the summer residence of a Cheshire brewer – dates to 1850, and was one of the first houses to be built on the promenade. It fell into the hands of Elyse's parents in the mid-1980s, who refurbished from top to toe, turning 23 small rooms into seven enormous suites. They didn't hold back – expect a grand Victorian feel with a dash of Belle Époque. You'll find Corinthian columns, crystal chandeliers, noble portraits on the walls, comfy sofas in front of the fire. Downstairs, there's a sitting room at the front with views of the bay, a bar in the middle for the daily papers, then curtains that open theatrically onto a muralled dining room at the back. Suites are huge – big sitting rooms, brass beds, claw-foot baths and walk-in showers. You'll find rugs on wood floors, ornate marble fireplaces, armchairs and sofas to take the strain; all but one have sea views. Bistro food waits downstairs, perhaps seared scallops, a rib-eye steak, baked toffee and chocolate sponge. There's off-road parking, too, and you can use the pool at the Empire, Osborne House's sister hotel. *Minimum stay: 2 nights at weekends.*

Rooms	7 suites for 2: £135–£195. Dinner, B&B £83–£110 p.p.
Meals	Lunch from £5. Dinner from £10.95. Afternoon tea from £8.50.
Closed	Christmas.

Elyse Waddy
Osborne House
Promenade, 17 North Parade,
Llandudno, LL30 2LP

Tel	+44 (0)1492 860330
Email	sales@osbornehouse.co.uk
Web	www.osbornehouse.co.uk

The Hand at Llanarmon

The Hand sits in glorious country – vast skies, rolling hills, country lanes that deliver you into the middle of nowhere. It's a popular place with walkers, mountain bikers and wildlife spotters, who spend their days having fun in the hills before rolling down to this 16th-century drovers' inn for the pleasures of a country local. A coal fire burns on the range in reception, a wood fire crackles in the front bar, a wood-burner keeps things cosy in the restaurant. Expect stone walls, low beamed ceilings, old pine settles and candles on the mantelpiece. There's a locals' bar for darts and pool, then a quiet sitting room for maps and books, which doubles as a treatment room. Delicious food draws a crowd, so grab a table and dig into excellent country fare, perhaps Welsh cheddar brûlée, roast rump of local lamb, sticky toffee pudding with caramel sauce. Airy rooms, all recently refurbished, have a contemporary feel with Welsh woollen throws on good beds and views of village and hill. Those in the main house are a little bigger, a couple have claw-foot-baths, three are dog friendly. Special indeed.

Rooms	11 doubles: £95–£135. 1 suite for 4: £150. Singles from £55. Sofabed £25.
Meals	Lunch & dinner £5–£30. Sunday lunch from £15.
Closed	Rarely.

Jackie & Jonathan Greatorex
The Hand at Llanarmon
Llanarmon Dyffryn Ceiriog,
Llangollen, LL20 7LD

Tel	+44 (0)1691 600666
Email	reception@thehandhotel.co.uk
Web	www.thehandhotel.co.uk

Plas Dinas Country House

The family home of Lord Snowdon dates to the 1600s and stands in 15 rural acres with an avenue of oak sweeping you up to the house. Princess Margaret often stayed and much of what fills the house belongs to the family: striking chandeliers, oils by the score, gilt-framed mirrors – an Aladdin's cave of beautiful things. There's a baby grand piano in the drawing room, where you find a roaring fire and an honesty bar, but potter about and find masses of memorabilia framed on the walls (make sure you visit the private dining room). Bedrooms – some with views across fields to the sea – mix a graceful past with modern design. You get four-posters, period colours, bold wallpapers, a sofa if there's room. A cute room in the eaves has mountain views, all have hot-water bottles, Apple TVs and excellent bathrooms, some with showers, others with free-standing baths. Good food waits in the restaurant, perhaps fishcakes with lime and ginger, lamb shank with a rosemary jus, chocolate tart with white chocolate ice-cream. Snowdon is close, as you'd expect, so bring walking boots and mountain bikes. *Minimum stay: 2 nights on bank holiday weekends. Extra beds £50.*

Rooms	3 doubles, 5 twin/doubles: £109-£169. 2 suites for 2: £159-£249.
Meals	Dinner, 3 courses, £25-£35.
Closed	23-27 December.

Neil Baines & Marco Soares
Plas Dinas Country House
Bontnewydd, Caernarfon, LL54 7YF
Tel   +44 (0)1286 830214
Email info@plasdinas.co.uk
Web   www.plasdinas.co.uk

Plas Bodegroes

A beautiful house, one of the loveliest places to stay in Wales. It may be far flung, but it's worth every second it takes to get here. Outside, six acres of mature gardens include a 200-year-old avenue of beech trees. Inside, a cool elegance roams freely: golden wallpapers, smouldering fires, a quirky bar that appears from thin air. French windows flood the house with light and open on to a veranda that comes wrapped in wisteria in summer. In good weather you take afternoon tea here while watching sheep graze in the fields; it's a little like being in a period drama. Bedrooms have chic fabrics, good beds, white linen, super bathrooms – it really doesn't matter which one you get. Some open onto a courtyard, a lovely spot for pre-dinner drinks in the evening. As for dinner, you eat in a dining room that doubles as an art gallery, a suitably theatrical spot for some very good food, perhaps braised pork cheek with crispy ham hock, wild sea bass with lemon and basil, cassis mousse with crème fraîche sorbet. The Llyn Peninsula waits: excellent walking, sandy beaches, towering cliffs. Pure heaven. *Pets by arrangement.*

Rooms	4 doubles, 3 twin/doubles: £120-£150. 3 suites for 2: £130-£150. Dinner, B&B £95-£125 p.p.
Meals	Dinner £45.
Closed	Sunday nights & Mondays.

Holly Kotkowicz
Plas Bodegroes
Efailnewydd, Pwllheli, LL53 5TH

Tel	+44 (0)1758 612363
Email	info@bodegroes.co.uk
Web	www.bodegroes.co.uk

Porth Tocyn Hotel

This family hotel is set in farmland with wake-up views over Cardigan Bay and the Snowdon mountain range. It's been in Nick's family for nearly 70 years – and the *Good Food Guide* forever too. He's passionate about the place and the food, and he and Louise are consummate hosts. Menus change daily: fresh fish aplenty, venison, guinea fowl, fruity puddings, Welsh cheeses – served in the dining room in front of a massive picture window for soaking up those views. Bedrooms are cosily inviting; some double rooms adjoin twins, easy for families of four or five, and cots are available too. Settle in any of the six interconnecting sitting rooms – all relaxed and friendly with heaps of art on the walls, flowers, country antiques, books and comfy cushioned places to read; there's a small bar and a children's snug with a games room next door. Spill out onto the front terrace on sunny days; there's an outdoor heated pool and tennis court and the coastal path runs right past the gardens. A great base for exploring the North Wales coast and mountains – seaside towns Abersoch, Pwllheli and Porthmadog are nearby. *Parking on-site.*

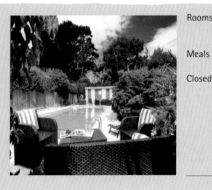

Rooms	2 doubles, 12 twin/doubles: £120–£200. 3 singles: £85–£100. Extra bed available.
Meals	Lunch from £11.95. Dinner, 3 courses with coffee & canapés, £49.
Closed	28 October – 16 March.

Nick Fletcher Brewer
Porth Tocyn Hotel
Bwlchtocyn, Pwllheli, LL53 7BU
Tel   +44 (0)1758 713303
Email   bookings@porthtocynhotel.co.uk
Web   www.porthtocynhotel.co.uk

Llwyndû Farmhouse

The view here is fabulous – a clean sweep across Cardigan Bay to the Llyn Peninsula beyond. Below, a ten-mile beach runs north to Harlech Point; behind, the Rhinog mountains rise. As for the farmhouse, it sits high on the hill and dates to 1581. It's a small, homespun world – Peter and Paula do it all themselves – a simple retreat with delicious slow food at the end of the day. Inside, you find thick stone walls, comfy sofas and a wood-burner in the inglenook. Bedrooms are scattered about. Those in the main house have a cosy feel with warm colours, low ceilings, perhaps a four-poster. Those in the outbuildings tend to be a little bigger and have painted stone walls, then ceilings open to the rafters. By day you explore the wonders of Snowdonia – you can climb mountains, take to cycle tracks or merely walk in the hills. By night you return to feast on local delights under ancient beams, perhaps Rhydlewis smoked salmon, Welsh Black steak, apple tarte tatin; if you're still hungry after that, excellent Welsh cheeses wait. Don't miss Portmeirion, or links golf at Harlech and Aberdovey. *Minimum stay: 2 nights.*

Rooms	3 doubles, 2 four-posters: £104–£126. 1 family room for 4: £104–£146. Dinner B&B from £82 p.p. Singles from £52.
Meals	Dinner £25–£30.
Closed	January.

Peter & Paula Thompson
Llwyndû Farmhouse
Llanaber, Barmouth, LL42 1RR

Tel	+44 (0)1341 280144
Email	intouch@llwyndu-farmhouse.co.uk
Web	www.llwyndu-farmhouse.co.uk

Entry 259   Map 5

Penmaenuchaf Hall

This grand old house sits high on the hill with fine views over the Mawddach estuary. It stands in 21 acres of woodlands and gardens, with daffodils, snowdrops and bluebells running riot in spring and a walled garden that bursts with colour in summer. The hall dates to 1865 and was home to a Bolton cotton merchant. Inside you find an open fire in the half-panelled hall, views of the estuary from the morning room, then a stunning drawing room, where mullioned windows frame views of water, mountain, sky. There's a tiny bar, a grand piano, sofas to sink into, country rugs on original wood floors. An airy restaurant opens onto a terrace, where you can eat in good weather, perhaps seared scallops, Welsh beef, apple tart and honey ice cream. Bedrooms have a homely country-house feel: comfy beds, warm colours, pretty fabrics, a wall of paper; some are huge, a couple have balconies. There's lots to do: 13 miles of river to fish, mountain bike trails, zip wires and cave tours. Cadair Idris is close (and far less crowded than Snowdon), so scale it for stunning views. Starry skies on clear nights delight. *Children over 6 welcome. Pets by arrangement.*

Rooms	7 doubles, 5 twin/doubles, 1 four-poster: £180-£310. 1 family room for 4: £275-£310. Singles £130-£195. Extra bed/sofabed £50-£60 per person per night.
Meals	Lunch from £6. Dinner, 3 courses, £28.50-£46. Afternoon tea from £7.95.
Closed	Rarely.

Mark Watson & Lorraine Fielding
Penmaenuchaf Hall
Penmaenpool, Dolgellau, LL40 1YB

Tel	+44 (0)1341 422129
Email	relax@penhall.co.uk
Web	www.penhall.co.uk

Y Meirionnydd

By day you explore the mighty wonders of Snowdonia, by night you return to this lovely small hotel and recover in style. It's one of those places that delivers just what you want; it's smart without being posh, the welcome is second to none, tasty food hits the spot, the bedrooms are excellent. You're in the middle of a small country town with a terrace at the front, so sit outside in summer and watch the world pass by. Inside, soft colours and warm lighting create a relaxed feel. There's a cute bar with armchairs and games, an airy breakfast room for the full Welsh works, then a smart restaurant cut into the rock, which was once the county jail; the food is somewhat better these days, perhaps game terrine with mustard piccalilli, rump of Welsh lamb with rosemary dumplings, Penderyn Welsh whisky and honey ice cream. Bedrooms upstairs fit the bill nicely. Some are bigger than others, but all have the same style: clean lines, cool colours, big beds, beautiful linen. You get the odd stone wall, an armchair if there's room, then super bathrooms. There's secure storage for bikes, too. *Minimum stay: 2 nights at weekends.*

Rooms	3 doubles, 2 twin/doubles: £89–£125. Singles £69–£79. Extra bed/sofabed £20 per person per night.
Meals	Dinner, 3 courses, £25. Not Mondays in low season.
Closed	One week at Christmas.

Marc Russell & Nick Banda
Y Meirionnydd
Smithfield Square, Dolgellau, LL40 1ES

Tel   +44 (0)1341 422554
Email   info@themeirionnydd.com
Web   www.themeirionnydd.com

The Bell at Skenfrith

The position here is magical: an ancient stone bridge, a river snaking through the valley, glorious hills rising beyond, cows grazing in lush fields. It's a perfect spot, not least because providence blessed it with this chic little inn. Inside, you find a locals' bar for the odd game of rugby, sofas in front of a wood-burner in the sitting room, then an airy restaurant for some very good food. In summer, doors fly open and life spills onto a stone terrace with views of hill and wood – a fine spot for lunch in the sun. Elegant country-house bedrooms brim with light. Some are beamed, most are big, you'll find padded bedheads, Farrow & Ball colours, perhaps a walnut bed or a claw-foot bath in your room. Those at the front have river views, those at the back look onto the hills, some have sofas, all have robes in excellent bathrooms. Seven circular walks start at the front door with maps to show you the way. Delicious food awaits your return, perhaps Welsh rarebit with a poached egg, braised beef brisket with dauphinoise potatoes, apple doughnuts with toffee sauce and mulled cider. *Minimum stay: 2 nights at weekends.*

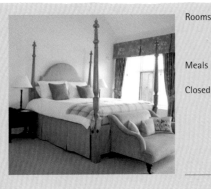

Rooms	5 doubles, 3 twin/doubles, 3 four-posters: £150-£230. Singles £90. Dinner, B&B £190-£270 per person.
Meals	Lunch from £5.95. Sunday lunch from £12.95. Dinner, 3 courses, around £35.
Closed	Rarely.

Richard Ireton & Sarah Hudson
The Bell at Skenfrith
Skenfrith, Abergavenny, NP7 8UH

Tel	+44 (0)1600 750235
Email	enquiries@skenfrith.co.uk
Web	www.skenfrith.co.uk

The Whitebrook

You're in the Wye valley, on a spur that takes you into the middle of nowhere, with birdsong and a gurgling stream supplying the soundtrack. It's a fairytale setting, a small house on a hillside in a forest that has conquered the valley. Light sparkles in ancient trees, footpaths meander through woods, the terrace for drinks before dinner has delightful views. As for the Whitebrook, it's a restaurant with rooms, where Chris whisks up incredible food – this must be the healthiest Michelin star you're likely to eat. His ethos is simple: take the best local produce, cook it without excessive embellishment, then draw out the cleanest expression of its flavour. It's gobsmacking stuff, lots of it foraged, perhaps Wye Valley asparagus with hogweed and pine; Hereford snails with aromatic flowers; suckling pig with hop shoots and artichokes; honey mousse with caramel and lemon Verbena. Rooms are a treat. Expect comfy beds, crisp linen, warm colours, excellent bathrooms; those at the front have valley views. You can walk in the forest, kayak on the Wye or explore Tintern Abbey. Hard to beat.

Rooms	6 doubles, 2 twin/doubles: £240-£399. Price includes dinner for 2.
Meals	Lunch (Wed-Sun) from £29-£47. Dinner, 3 courses, included; non-residents £59. Tasting menu (obligatory Fri & Sat) £74.
Closed	1-17 January.

	Chris & Kirsty Harrod
	The Whitebrook
	Whitebrook, Monmouth, NP25 4TX
Tel	+44 (0)1600 860254
Email	info@thewhitebrook.co.uk
Web	www.thewhitebrook.co.uk

32 Townhouse

Narberth is lovely – quirky and colourful, lively and independent. It's wrapped up in Pembrokeshire's rolling hills with the coast and its path waiting ten miles south. As for this stylish restaurant with rooms, it sits on the high street, dates to 1820, and has a smart Georgian exterior with early Victorian bay windows. Inside, the style is hard to miss: Russian red in the bar with a picture of Gorbachev on the wall; then period green in the restaurant, where gilt-framed oils hang by the score. Potter about and find original tiles and ironwork, parquet floors and stained glass windows; the zinc-topped bar was made from a Methodist pulpit. There's a conservatory bistro that opens onto a pretty terrace for strong coffee, homemade quiche and posh burgers. Bedrooms above are soundproofed and come with smart beds, white linen, travertine bathrooms and attractive prices; some interconnect, others in the eaves have the odd beam. Delicious food waits downstairs, perhaps calamari with chorizo and fennel, chicken with braised shallots, toffee apple and blackberry crumble. A great little base.

Rooms	6 doubles, 2 twin/doubles: £85-£190.
Meals	Lunch from £4.95. Light bites from £7.45. Dinner, 3 courses, about £30.
Closed	23-26 December.

Dominic Swingler
32 Townhouse
32 High Street, Narberth, SA67 7AS
Tel   +44 (0)1834 218338
Email   info@32townhouse.com
Web   www.32townhouse.com

Penally Abbey

This beautifully refurbished country-house hotel sits high on the hill with long views over Carmarthen Bay. Outside, there's a small courtyard, then five acres of lawns and woodland, where bluebells run riot in spring. Inside, chic interiors come with cool colours, painted panelling, parquet flooring and the odd Doric column. There's an elegant bar in deep charcoal with fine art on the walls, then a big drawing room with an open fire and huge sea views. Big windows in the main house flood the rooms with light, while doors in the sunroom open onto a gravelled terrace, where you can read the papers, dig into afternoon tea, or fall asleep in the sun. Bedrooms have a stunning new look: off-white walls, beautiful beds, crisp white linen, elegant fabrics. Big rooms in the main house have vast windows to frame the view, all have sublime white marble bathrooms. You eat in style in the restaurant – period colours, grand chandelier – perhaps steamed clams with lemon and ginger, chicken with chestnuts and a pear tarte tatin, a dark chocolate tort with pistachio ice cream. There's fine coastal walking, too. *Pets by arrangement.*

Rooms	3 doubles, 6 twin/doubles, 2 four-posters: £145-£265. Dinner, B&B from £90 p.p.
Meals	Lunch from £5. Dinner, 3 courses, £30-£35. Sunday lunch from £14.95.
Closed	Rarely.

Melanie & Lucas Boissevain
Penally Abbey
Penally, Tenby, SA70 7PY

Tel	+44 (0)1834 843033
Email	enquiries@schoolroomcottage.co.uk
Web	www.penally-abbey.com

Stackpole Inn

This lovely inn sits in a village that's marooned in beautiful country. It's a few miles back from the sea, with Barafundle Bay – one of the finest beaches in Britain – a very short drive away. You can pick up the coastal path, too, and follow it round past Stackpole Quay and St Govan's Chapel to the cliffs at Linney Head, then the surfers at Freshwater West. It's pure heaven, one of those sleepy areas you drop into for a couple of days and hardly use your car. As for the Stackpole, it's a great little base – stylish and welcoming with tasty rustic food, perhaps deep-fried whitebait, rib of local beef, almond and hazelnut tart. Outside, the pub is drenched in honeysuckle and there's a small garden to the front for a drop of Welsh ale in summer. Inside, you find low wooden ceilings, exposed stone walls, a hard-working wood-burner and four hand pumps at the slate bar. Super bedrooms have comfy beds, stripped floors, seaside colours and excellent bathrooms. All have sofabeds, two have velux windows for star gazing. Dogs and children are very welcome.

Rooms	2 twin/doubles: £90. 2 family rooms for 4: £90–£120. Singles from £60.
Meals	Lunch from £5. Dinner, 3 courses, £25–£30. Sunday lunch, 3 courses, £18.95.
Closed	Rarely.

Gary & Becky Evans
Stackpole Inn
Stackpole, Pembroke, SA71 5DF
Tel   +44 (0)1646 672324
Email   info@stackpoleinn.co.uk
Web   www.stackpoleinn.co.uk

Crug Glas

St Davids is one of the most magical places in Britain. It sits in Pembroke's national park, has an imperious 12th-century cathedral, and is surrounded by magnificent coastline that's dotted with cliffs and vast sandy beaches. As for Janet's wonderful retreat, it's part chic hotel, part farmhouse B&B, stylish yet personal, a great place to stay. The house dates from 1120 and sits in 600 acres of arable and grazing land (they rear cattle and grow cereals). Outside, you find lawns and a small copse sprinkled with bluebells, then field and sky, and that's about it. Inside, there's an honesty bar in the sitting room and a Welsh dresser in the dining room, where Janet serves delicious food: homemade soups, home-reared beef, chocolate mousse with clotted cream. Fancy bedrooms are the big surprise: a vast four-poster, the odd copper bath, old armoires, beautiful fabrics. All have robes in gorgeous bathrooms, bigger rooms come with sofas, one room occupies most of the top floor. Two rooms in an old barn have exposed timbers and underfloor heating. The coast is about five fields to the west.

Rooms	5 doubles, 2 twin/doubles: £150–£190. Singles £110–£140.
Meals	Lunch, 2 courses, from £18. Dinner, 3 courses, £25–£30. Sunday lunch £22.50. Afternoon tea from £12.50.
Closed	22-27 December.

Janet & Perkin Evans
Crug Glas
Solva, Haverfordwest, SA62 6XX

Tel	+44 (0)1348 831302
Email	info@crug-glas.co.uk
Web	www.crug-glas.co.uk

The Manor Town House

Fishguard is quirky – arty and friendly with a folk festival in May and a jazz festival in August. You'll find great coastal walks, sandy beaches and magical St Davids a few miles south. In short, it's much more than an overnight stop on your way to Ireland and, with a happy vibe waiting at the Manor Town House, hard to resist. Chris and Helen escaped London and have taken to their new world like ducks to water. Inside, you're greeted by a couple of gorgeous sitting rooms – stripped floorboards, cool colours, local art, and crackling fires in winter. One has an honesty bar, you get fresh flowers, lots of books, and comfy sofas from which to plan your day. Homely bedrooms have lots of charm: bold colours, beautiful fabrics, the odd antique, super-comfy beds. Those at the back have sea views, perhaps a sofa or a padded window seat, while compact bathrooms do the trick. Breakfast is a treat, there's a garden for afternoon tea overlooking the harbour, and it's a one-minute stroll up the road to Bar Five for cocktails. Pembrokeshire awaits. Brilliant.
Minimum stay: 2 nights at weekends in summer.

Rooms	2 doubles, 3 twin/doubles: £105-£135. Single room available from £80. Extra bed/sofabed £20 p.p. per night.
Meals	Restaurants within 100m. Packed lunches £10.
Closed	23-27 December.

Chris & Helen Sheldon
The Manor Town House
11 Main Street, Fishguard, SA65 9HG
Tel   +44 (0)1348 873260
Email   enquiries@manortownhouse.com
Web   www.manortownhouse.com

Llys Meddyg

This beautiful small hotel has a little bit of everything: chic bedrooms that pack a punch, a cellar bar for cocktails before dinner, a stylish restaurant for delicious local food. In summer you decant into the garden, where a café/bistro opens up for coffee and cake or pizza from a wood-fired oven. There's a smokehouse out here, too, then a yurt tucked away around the corner that comes with a wood-burner and a hot tub. It's an intimate place, where staff stop to chat, where locals pop in for a coffee, where you can take home a jar of quince jelly made by Ed's mum. Food lies at the heart of the affair and you eat in a stylish restaurant with Welsh art on the walls, perhaps home-smoked salmon, slow-cook lamb, caramelized pear with blue-cheese ice-cream. Beautiful bedrooms are scattered about. Those in the main house have cool colours, vast beds and fancy bathrooms. Those in the mews have a rustic feel and garden views; all have fluffy bath robes. Pembrokeshire's coastal path waits for windswept cliffs and sandy beaches. Don't miss St Davids or the Preseli Hills. Dogs are very welcome. *Minimum stay: 2 nights at weekends.*

Rooms	8 doubles: £100–£180. 1 yurt for 2: £100–£120. Singles from £85.
Meals	Lunch from £7. Dinner from £14.
Closed	Rarely.

Louise & Edward Sykes
Llys Meddyg
East Street, Newport, SA42 0SY

Tel	+44 (0)1239 820008
Email	info@llysmeddyg.com
Web	www.llysmeddyg.com

Gliffaes Hotel

A charming country-house hotel that towers above the river Usk as it pours through the valley below. In summer, doors open onto a large terrace, where you can sit in the sun and soak up the view – red kites circle above, sheep graze beyond. You're in 35 peaceful acres of formal lawns and mature woodland. Inside, interiors pack a punch. Afternoon tea 'on the house' is served every day in the panelled sitting room – family portraits hang on the wall, logs crackle in the grandest fireplace. This is a well-known fishing hotel and fishermen often gather in the bar for a quick drink and a tall tale. Eventually, they spin into the restaurant and dig into lovely seasonal food (the hotel is part of the Slow Food Movement), perhaps goat's cheese soufflé, fillet of halibut, lemon tart with passion fruit sorbet. Country-house bedrooms wait above. Expect smart fabrics, warm colours, crisp linen, fresh flowers. Several have river views, a couple have small balconies, one has a claw-foot bath that overlooks the front lawn. Outside, beautiful gardens include a small arboretum of specimen trees. Wonderful. *Minimum stay: 2 nights at weekends.*

Rooms	19 twin/doubles: £115–£298. 4 singles: £115–£145. Dinner, B&B £137–£187 per person. Extra bed/sofabed £25 p.p. per night.
Meals	Light lunches from £5. Dinner, 3 courses, £42. Sunday lunch £22–£29.
Closed	29 December – 25 January.

	James & Susie Suter
	Gliffaes Hotel
	Gliffaes Road, Crickhowell, NP8 1RH
Tel	+44 (0)1874 730371
Email	calls@gliffaeshotel.com
Web	www.gliffaeshotel.com

The Felin Fach Griffin

So what are the ingredients of one of the loveliest inns in the land? Well, it's quirky, homespun, and thrives on a mix of relaxed informality and colourful style. The bar resembles the sitting room of a hip country house, with timber frames, cool tunes and comfy sofas in front of the fire. Painted stone walls come in blocks of colour and you dine informally in the white-walled restaurant, with stock pots simmering on an Aga. The food is excellent, perhaps Portland crab, boeuf Bourguignon, chocolate mousse with mascarpone; much of what you eat comes from a half-acre kitchen garden, with meat and game from the hills around you. Pretty bedrooms have colour and style. Expect comfy beds and crisp linen, good bathrooms with fluffy towels, Roberts radios and a smattering of books (but no TVs). Breakfast is a leisurely treat: read the morning papers, make your own toast, scoff the full Welsh works. A road passes outside, but quietly at night, while lanes lead into the hills, so come to walk, ride, bike, canoe. Hay is close for books galore. Don't miss excellent off-season deals.

Rooms	3 doubles, 3 twin/doubles: £135–£207. 1 family room for 3: £175–£232. Singles £110–£137. Dinner, B&B £192–£232 per person. Extra bed/sofabed £25 p.p. per night.
Meals	Lunch from £12. Dinner, 3 courses, from £25–£30. Sunday lunch from £12.50.
Closed	Christmas Eve & Day (evening) & 4 days in January.

	Charles & Edmund Inkin
	The Felin Fach Griffin
	Felin Fach, Brecon, LD3 0UB
Tel	+44 (0)1874 620111
Email	enquiries@felinfachgriffin.co.uk
Web	www.felinfachgriffin.co.uk

Entry 271   Map 2

Lake Country House & Spa

An elegant country-house hotel lost in beautiful hills with deep peace all around. Fifty acres of lawns, lakes and ancient woodland wrap around you, there's a spa with treatment rooms, an indoor pool and a tennis court by the lake. You can sit in a hot tub and watch guests fish for their supper, try your luck on the nine-hole golf course, saddle up nearby and take to the hills. Come home to afternoon tea in the old-school drawing room, where an archipelago of rugs warms a brightly polished wood floor and chandeliers hang from the ceiling. The hotel opened over a hundred years ago; leather-bound fishing logs date to 1894. A feel of the 1920s lingers. Fires come to life in front of your eyes, grand pianos and grandfather clocks sing their songs, snooker balls knock about in the distance. Dinner is a treat, perhaps crab with wasabi ice cream, duck with fennel and honey, blood orange cheesecake with chocolate sorbet. Lovely rooms wait. Most are suites: those in the house are warmly traditional, those in the lodge softly contemporary. The London train takes four hours and stops in the village.

Rooms	6 twin/doubles: £195. 24 suites for 2: £240–£260. Singles from £145. Dinner, B&B (min. 2 nights) from £122.50 p.p.
Meals	Lunch, 3 courses, £22.50. Dinner, 4 courses, £38.50.
Closed	Never.

Jean–Pierre Mifsud
Lake Country House & Spa
Llangammarch Wells, LD4 4BS
Tel   +44 (0)1591 620202
Email   info@lakecountryhouse.co.uk
Web   www.lakecountryhouse.co.uk

Milebrook House Hotel

An old-school, country-house hotel with three acres of gardens that run down to the river Teme. You'll find Wales on one side and England on the other, so bring your wellies and wade across; the walking is magnificent. The house was once home to writer Wilfred Thesiger; his friend, Haile Selassie, visited in the 1920s. These days it's informally run by three generations of the Marsden family with Beryl and Rodney leading the way. Step inside and enter a world that's rooted in a delightful past: clocks tick, cats snooze, fires crackle, the odd champagne cork escapes its bondage. Beautiful art hangs on the walls, the sitting room is stuffed with books, the bar comes in country-house style, and there's food to reckon with in the dining room, perhaps local pigeon with caramelised apple, slow-roasted shoulder of Welsh lamb, apple crumble and butterscotch sundae. A kitchen garden supplies much for the table. You can fish, spot deer in the woods, play croquet on the lawn. Red kite, moorhens, kingfishers and herons live in the valley. Homely bedrooms wait. Presteigne and Ludlow are close.

Rooms	5 doubles, 5 twins: £144. 1 family room for 3: £172. Singles from £87.50. Dinner, B&B from £102.50 per person.
Meals	Lunch, 2 courses, £14.95; not Monday. Dinner, 3 courses, £30–£35. Sunday lunch from £17.
Closed	Rarely.

Rodney, Beryl & Joanne Marsden
Milebrook House Hotel
Stanage, Knighton, LD7 1LT

Tel	+44 (0)1547 528632
Email	hotel@milebrookhouse.co.uk
Web	www.milebrookhouse.co.uk

Quick reference indices

Wheelchair-accessible
At least one bedroom and bathroom accessible for wheelchair users. Phone for details.

England

Scotland

Wales

Children of all ages welcome
These owners have told us that they welcome children of all ages. Please note cots and highchairs may not necessarily be available.

England

Pets welcome
Pets welcome; please let the
owner know if you want to
bring pets.

England

Quick reference indices

Channel Islands

Scotland

Wales

Swimming pool

Swimming pool on the premises; use may be by arrangement.

England

Channel Islands

Wales

Gwynedd 258

Powys 272

Bikes to hire or borrow
Bikes on the premises to hire or borrow.

England
Cornwall 24 • 31

Cumbria 32 • 33 • 37 • 41

Devon 59 • 61

Dorset 71

Essex 81 • 82

Gloucestershire 85

Hampshire 86 • 89

Herefordshire 91

Isle of Wight 96 • 97

Norfolk 125

Oxfordshire 134 • 136

Rutland 143 • 144

Shropshire 150

Somerset 155 • 159

Suffolk 166

Sussex 175

Yorkshire 203

Scotland
Argyll & Bute 212 • 213 • 214 • 215

Dumfries & Galloway 218 • 219

Edinburgh 222

Highland 229

Perth & Kinross 242

Wales
Powys 270

Tennis court
Tennis court on the premises; use may be by arrangement.

England
Bath & N.E. Somerset 6

Berkshire 7

Cornwall 22 • 30

Cumbria 32 • 33

Devon 59

Dorset 76

Essex 82

Hampshire 86

Isle of Wight 97

Norfolk 123

Rutland 143

Sussex 175

Worcestershire 195

Yorkshire 203

Channel Islands
Guernsey 208

Scotland
Argyll & Bute 215

Wales
Gwynedd 258

Powys 270 • 272

Public transport
These places are within 10 miles of a bus/train station and owner can arrange collection, with notice.

England
Bath & N.E. Somerset 1 • 2 • 3 • 4 • 5 • 6

Berkshire 7

Brighton & Hove 8 • 9 • 10 • 11

Bristol 12

Quick reference indices

Quick reference indices

Photo: Talland Bay Hotel, entry 15

Photo: Chewton Glen, entry 86

Alastair Sawday has been publishing books for over 20 years, finding Special Places to Stay in Britain and abroad. All our properties are inspected by us and are chosen for their charm and individuality. And there are many more to explore on our perennially popular website: www.sawdays.co.uk. You can buy any of our books at a reader discount of 25%* on the RRP.

List of titles:	RRP	Discount price
British Bed & Breakfast	£15.99	£11.99
British Hotels and Inns	£15.99	£11.99
Pubs & Inns of England & Wales	£15.99	£11.99
Dog-friendly Breaks in Britain	£14.99	£11.24
French Bed & Breakfast	£15.99	£11.99
French Châteaux & Hotels	£15.99	£11.99
Italy	£15.99	£11.99

*postage and packaging is added to each order

How to order:
Call: **+44 (0)117 204 7810**

Photo: The Old Court House, entry 209

Index by property name 323

Photo: Artist Residence Penzance, entry 23

Photo: Driftwood Hotel, entry 18

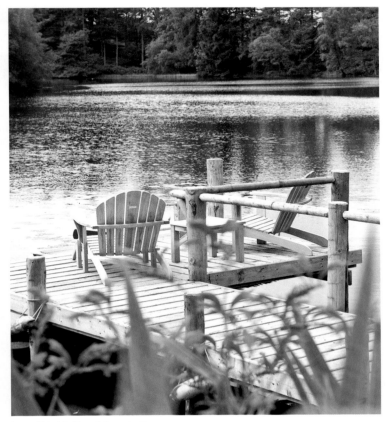

Photo: Gilpin Lake House & Spa, entry 43